Acky

ACKY

by

George Ewart Evans

FABER AND FABER
3 Queen Square
London

First published in 1973
by Faber and Faber Limited
3 Queen Square London WC1
Printed in Great Britain by
Latimer Trend & Company Ltd Plymouth

ISBN 0 571 08418 4

120928

Foreword

You won't find the names of Akerman Flatt and his wife, Sarah, in any parish register. But there were many more like them in the Suffolk villages shortly after the last war—couples who had brought up a family and who were now living by themselves. Acky and Sarah lived in a thatched cottage (unrestored) at the edge of the broad heathland of Fenhall—a village you won't find on any map, either.

Acky is one of the survivors of those men who retired after the horses left the farms in the early fifties. He still has much of his old vigour and is likely to reach his eighty-fifth—maybe even his ninetieth—birthday. But most of the events recorded here happened to him during the few years after he had finished working on the farm.

Contents

I

Cousin Belinda

They were talking pigs in the bar of the *Plough* at Fenhall. A thick mist had earlier drifted inland off the sea, and there was no likelihood of anyone else dropping in that night and interrupting a serious conversation. There was Acky, Job Summers the landlord, Tom Downey, the stockman from Firtree Farm and Jim Burrows, Acky's near neighbour on the Common. It was just after the last war when meat was still rationed; and a Ministry man was likely to come round at any time asking how many pigs you kept. One of them had called on Acky, earlier on when rationing had just begun. Acky told him:

"You go down there to my sties and see for yourself. There they are. The pigs, do you follow that fence; and when you git there do you count their legs and divide by four. I reckon you won't be far wrong then, mister."

Pigs were meat, and for that reason were even more valuable than a man's reputation; and there was a great deal of serious and secret thought about pigs. Jim Burrows was sitting nearest the fire which made his round face redder than ever:

"Have you seen Fred Partridge from Fordham recently, Acky?" he asked.

"No, I ain't done business with him, nor ain't seen him since Christmas."

"Fred's busy," said Tom Downey, after he'd had a pull at his beer. "His wife's expectin' a baby and Fred's expectin' pigs."

Cousin Belinda

After the laugh which pleased Tom very much, the landlord said:

"It must be that sow you sold him, Acky."

"I reckon so. She were a good 'un, and she'll bring off a rare litter if I know hogs. I hope owd Fred won't count 'em too close and will manage to slip me one on 'em. But you better git back from the fire, Tom," Acky said to the stockman. "Don't aim to set as near to it as Jim there. Your water-boots fare begin to pong; we could a'most be down in Firtree."

"What's the matter with my boots?" Tom Downey protested loudly, looking at his Wellingtons. "Or what's the matter with you, most like, Acky? You're allus a-picking on 'em!"

"And I reckon your wife do, Tom," Jim Burrows said, winking at Acky. "I never see you without 'em: I reckon you must wear 'em in bed."

"I'm sick o' you lot," Tom rose suddenly and placed his glass down on the bar. "Give me another pint, Joby. I reckon a man got to have something to make him forget he has to set with this lot!"

"Set you down, Tom. I'll get it," Job Summers soothed him. And as he drew the beer he said in a different tone: "Keep to pigs, lads! You can't go wrong if you keep to pigs."

Job the landlord brought the beer over to Tom who took a good pull at it.

"That's whoolly right, Joby," said Acky. "Keep to pigs! I reckon there are two main things a man should allus be faithful to—his wife and his pigs. Maybe it's his pigs and his wife; but that's another line o' country and we don't want to go exploring into thet now. Pigs are a'most human; and I seen more sense in some on 'em than I see in many who's dressed in trousers, and go round with no more brains atween their ears than you could put in an egg-spoon. If you stick by hogs and treat 'em well, they'll allus stick by you."

Shortly after Acky's little sermon Job Summers stood up.

"That's it, boys. Time to turn in," and the group broke up. But pigs were still in Acky's thoughts as he sat down to his supper, and he told his wife, Sarah, about the talk in the *Plough*. But Sarah cut him short:

"I'm off to bed. If you and your pigs can't give me rest, I'm going to seek it for myself. That's all I hear: pigs from break-fast till bedtime. I don't want to see another pig in my life." And she creaked up the narrow stairs without giving Acky time to get the last word in.

As it happened, however, in less than a week Sarah was forced to swallow her words about pigs. The trouble began when Acky strained his back lifting a bag of meal on to his bicycle to bring it home from Fordham. He was in bed for three weeks, and Sarah had to feed the livestock with only occasional help from Jim Burrows.

When at last Acky came downstairs and started to move about, he was so thankful to be on his feet again that he said to Sarah:

"You can have one of the pigs, gel. You bin right handy a-feeding 'em and seeing to 'em while I been a-bedded."

Sarah took him at his word: chose one of the young pigs and decided to rear it herself. She had never tended pigs before Acky's accident; had never been near the sties. But now she had become interested; and it wasn't surprising therefore that the pig she reared grew into one of the finest sows that had ever been in Acky's stock.

Its first litter, under Sarah's management, came on like champions. There were nine of them; and they were all as fat as butter. One day, the postman happened to take a glance at them as he was passing. They were all lying side by side in the sty—they were so fat they couldn't lie in any other way—

and they looked what they were, a row of winners. After the postman had seen them their fame soon got abroad, and offers were coming in as fast as Sarah could deal with them. But everyone who came to the house, hoping to buy a couple of the pigs, first approached Acky, thinking the litter belonged to him. Acky was very scathing:

"You must see ma wife about the pigs. She picked the best pig in one of my litters; and now she's a-making her fortune. I fare to think I larned her better'n I know myself. Sarah!" he called out, "there's some'un else come to fill you stocking for you."

But Sarah was at least as good on the business side as Acky; and she sold seven of the young pigs at an excellent price, keeping two she'd picked for herself. Acky got quite depressed and jealous of Sarah's success, and he did more than his usual amount of thinking. For, as he said, it was a hard thing for a man to spend half his lifetime a-rearing of pigs, and then to be beaten at the game by a mere beginner who—to start with at any rate—hardly knew one end of a pig from the other. And it made it no easier to reflect that the beginner was his own wife. But Acky had always told himself:

"There's suthen comforting in pigs. Whenever I git the Black Jack a-setting on my shoulders I go out and look at ma pigs. And that whoolly eases me. I feel a new man, jus' through taking a peek at my best hog and a-feeling the good bacon that's a-growing on its back."

On this occasion he took his own advice and went outside to the pigsty and leaned over its side. But it was one of Sarah's pigs he was looking at this time.

Later that night, as Sarah sat knitting for one of the grandchildren, Acky said with great deliberation:

"One o' those small pigs o' yourn would make good pork, gel. I was looking at him this afternoon."

"Would it now?" Sarah said tartly. "But it's not going up to the factory yet, you ma' depend."

"No need for it to go the factory. They wouldn't give more'n a flea-bite for it up there, gel."

"What do you mean? It's not legal to kill it anywhere else! You're not thinking . . ."

"Yeh, that's just what I'm a-thinking. We can see to the pig here, and make twice as much for him as we would if we sent him to Ipsidge."

Now this was the time of rationing and innumerable restrictions, and Sarah said virtuously: "But that ain't legal, Akerman Flatt."

"What's legal?" said Acky. "It's only the way o' doing things these smart fellers in the town cook up for their own sort o' convenience. It's a poor way o' going on if a man can't kill his own pig when he wants to. Us country chaps—where would we be now if we paid too much regard to *legal*?"

"It's taken you a long time to think up them sentiments, Acky Flatt. Your pigs have been going up the factory since the beginning of the war."

"But you got to go slow in these things and kinda think round everything."

"And what, might I ask, is at the middle of all this thinking?"

"One o' your pigs, I reckon, Sarah," Acky said, with a grin. "But don't you go ahid now! It would be something if we could sell him on the side. We could let Jim Burrows into the scheme. He could fix it up with one of the butchers in Fordham; and no one else need know a thing."

At first Sarah would have nothing to do with Acky's plan, especially as it was one of her pigs that was to start it off. But Acky was a persuasive talker when he was roused; and after working on Sarah for a couple of evenings the pig's fate was

settled. Acky met Jim Burrows one morning; and on that
same day they killed the pig; and it was soon trussed up in
Acky's shed, under lock and key, with not a bristle of it lying
about to betray what had happened. That night, when all the
lights were out in the cottages round the Common, a van from
Fordham drew up near Acky's place; and that was the last
Sarah saw of her pig.

The money—all in pound notes—that Acky brought in a
few days later was considerable, and made Sarah open her eyes
wider than usual. Acky saw how things were and before the
end of the week he was talking about Sarah's other pig; and
this time Sarah was listening, right from the beginning. In a
short while they were seeing to it in exactly the same way as
its companion. Acky and Jim Burrows made a rare job of it,
and left it in the shed for the van to collect on the following
night, just as they'd done before.

But there was one big difference from the first time. In the
village of Fenhall, you might if you are very careful do something *once* without anyone knowing anything about it at all.
If, however, you plan to do the same thing twice, still hoping
to keep it a close secret, you may as well do it in the middle of
the Common before the eyes of the whole village. You'd save
yourself a lot of trouble. There's a saying in Fenhall that sums
it up completely: If you want to keep a secret in a village, you
got to tell nine people.

Akerman Flatt should have known all this before he killed
the second pig. He did, of course; but the money Sarah and he
had gathered from the first one had charmed away all his
caution. The charm was broken the morning Jim Burrows
came pelting across the Common, crashed his bike against the
fence and panted up to Acky who was digging in his garden.

"The pig, Acky!" he burst out. "Looks as if some kind
friend has done us a good turn. There's an inspector bloke

down the pub this moment. Joe Easy spotted him; he knew the number of his car. I reckon he went in to find out where your place is."

Acky stabbed his spade into the ground and walked away from it. "Come in, Jim," he said quietly.

"What are you going to do, Acky? We ain't got time to bury him. This bloke from the Ministry will be over at any time, I doubt."

Acky was fingering his ear-ring. Then he said to Sarah:

"Get three o' your bed-sheets, gel, and hang 'em on the linen line. We'll have him in here from the shed, Jim—here's the key—as soon as Sarah's got the sheets up."

Screened from the Common by the sudden access of washing on Sarah's line, they got the carcass in quickly and laid it on the sofa in the living-room.

"You go now, Jim," Acky said calmly, "and if you see this inspector bloke on the Common keep him a-talking; and tell him we got a very important wisitor."

A few minutes later Acky, standing by the window, saw a man making purposefully for his front gate. As he came up the path Acky shouted to Sarah:

"Is the soup ready, gel? I'll take it up to her if it is." And when the knock came at the door, Acky opened it immediately, saying politely: "Come in, sir; come in. We've been expecting on you."

Now this hit the inspector right between the eyes as it was meant to do. "Expecting me?" he asked, hesitating on the doorstep.

"Aren't you the doctor then?"

"No, I'm from the Ministry of Food. I . . . are you Mr. Flatt?"

"Yeh, Akerman Flatt. But come in all the same," Acky said benevolently, showing the man to a chair in the living-room.

Then calling over his shoulder to Sarah who was still in the kitchen: "That's a rum 'un now! I thought this gentleman was Dr. Bulley's loco. Set yourself down, sir. We're all of a muddle this morning. Cousin Belinda came over from Frannigan yesterday. She bin a-physicing for some long while, but she were took bad last night, right bad." He tapped his chest significantly: "The heart it is, I reckon. You'd better take the soup up to her yourself, gel."

The inspector showed a polite interest as Sarah carried the tray up the narrow stairs. Then he turned to Acky and asked him curtly: "You keep pigs, Mr. Flatt?"

Acky laughed:

"Yeh, yeh. I've been a-schemin' for some while to make the pigs keep me, but I ain't made much headway yet. You better come and see 'em for yourself. Easier than talking about 'em."

For the next ten minutes Acky showed the inspector round his sties while he took notes of what he saw. Only once did he act as though he had any suspicions: he was coming back into the house when he folded up like a jack-knife and peered into an empty bucket that happened to be outside the door of the kitchen. Then after a glance round the garden the inspector nodded at the cottage. "Four rooms?" he asked pleasantly.

"Yeh, plenty of room for us togither now the family is off-hand. But you better come in."

Acky took him through the kitchen where Sarah was washing the bowl that had contained the soup.

"She ate it!" said Acky. "Good, she'll feel the benefit o' that."

The inspector was looking up at the ceiling of the kitchen and Acky asked him:

"You interested in owd beams?"

"Yes, I am. I expect this is quite an old cottage."

"Oh yeh, it's old enough, I reckon."

"And I expect you got some fine beams in the upstairs rooms," the inspector added, smiling at Sarah.

"Yeh, there's some rare 'uns up there," said Acky. "You're welcome to have a look at 'em. Cousin Belinda's in one o' the rooms but we can jus' go up and have a peek at 'em."

"Oh, please don't bother."

"Thet's all right. How does she fare this morning, Sarah?"

"She's now a-sleeping," Sarah said very quietly.

"Well, come you on, sir. We can jus' take a quick look at the ceiling without disturbing her."

The two men creaked gently up the stairs, Acky leading. He showed the inspector the queerly shaped beams in their own bedroom first. "Ships' timbers, so they reckon," said Acky, "taken off the wrecks." Then he went to the door of the second bedroom and bent his head to listen.

"Belinda! Belinda!" he called softly; and when there was no answer: "She's still asleep." Softly he opened the door and nodded to the man behind him. The room was sparsely furnished; but there was a huge double-bed in its centre. It was covered with a white overlay that rose to Cousin Belinda's evidently ample form. She was wearing some sort of nightcap; and the sheet was covering her face. She was lying as still as death. "She git right down into the clothes," Acky whispered, "sleeping peaceably!" And he raised his hand to indicate the blackened beams and rafters. "She fare better now she's rested."

The inspector nodded and after another glance at the form in the bed followed Acky out, and downstairs into the living-room.

The inspector now took up his hat, saying with a friendly nod:

B   *17*

"Thank you, Mr. Flatt; most interesting. But . . . I should tell you: we had a report to say you'd been killing a pig."

Acky raised his eyebrows and gave a deep chuckle as Sarah nervously played with the hem of her apron: "Killing a pig! Why I couldn't do a thing like thet. It ain't legal. I couldn't do thet!"

"No, no, no," the inspector agreed, as he opened the door.

"You mustn't listen to all these reports thet go round, mister, most on 'em are from blank cartridges," Acky said, looking at the inspector gravely. "And some 'un's allus ready to do you a good turn in these parts." He laughed again: "We're a nice neighbourly lot out here when you come to it. No, sir, we cut one another's throats not the pigs'!"

When the inspector's car had pulled off the Common, Acky said to Sarah:

"Belinda better stay in bed, gel, until the van come to fetch her. Phew! that were a right close 'un!"

But Sarah was still in a turmoil.

"I'll never do anything like that again! You're a rogue, Akerman Flatt; and you get other people mixed up in your roguery. I never want to see another pig in my life. There! My poor owd heart is a-going like a kittle-drum!"

Acky looked at her calmly.

"I know 'xactly how you feel, gel." Then he sat down on the sofa. "I reckon you're right—but take it easy, take it easy—that's what I allus been a-saying about pigs. Pigs is very troublesome, chance times. It'll be much quieter and easier for you, I reckon, to keep to your hins and your guinea-fowl."

2

The Coin

After Acky Flatt retired from the farm he spent a good deal of his time walking round the Common. He was up there so often with his old lurcher he called *Bundler* that he became known in Fenhall as the *Keeper*; and they used to say there wasn't a caterpillar up there he didn't know well. He'd be there just after dawn, and again in the evening, often standing against an old elder-bush, as still as a stone, watching what was going on, and sizing up the birds, the rabbits and an occasional hare that came out after dusk. On his way up to the heathland he passed the school; and he would often stop to have a chat with the schoolmaster, Mr. Robertson, whenever he happened to be out in the schoolhouse garden.

The schoolmaster was a Scot and interested in the new area he had come to: he liked talking to Acky about the farming customs he knew in Scotland when he was a boy. Acky had frequently mentioned him to Sarah:

"Thet Mr. Robertson is some clever. He read a rare lot o' books; and he's allus asking questions. But he's a-willing to larn; and it's a right pleasure to hev a word or two with him now and again."

"I hope you not a-telling him a lot o' thet owd squit you try to load off on to me!"

"Now then!" Acky answered. "Don't you git windy over nawthen! I allus tell him what I know—leastways, most of it.

He's on about the owd farming, and I'm of the same mind as him there. They don't farm like they used to, he say; and I tell him the way they're a-going on now will soon be the ruination o' the land."

"It 'pears to me," said Sarah, "you together is like an open-air sewing meeting, going at it like a pair o' milliners. It's a pity Mr. Robertson don't do more digging and less talking. He's not got his garden round yet."

"You must ha' got up the wrong side o' the bed this marning, gel. Give the man time! He's only been here a year, and he got suthen else to see to asides his garden. But do you know what he say to me? He's allus polite and he call me Mr. Flatt. Howsomever, he say to me last week: 'Akerman, that's a very interesting name; a rare name and a very old one,' he say. And I towd him:

" 'I reckon it is. It were my grandfather's second name; and he weren't born yesterday!'

" 'Well,' he say, 'it's a name that's six or seven hundred year old. I see it writ in the documents.' "

Sarah looked at him severely.

"You're romancing again, Acky! You better keep to boasting about your owd yard to Mr. Robertson, and steer away from books and all thet."

"Ma heart alive!" said Acky. "If you were a man, us together would have to call you Thomas! Here it is!" he added, taking a grubby piece of paper out of his pocket. "He writ it down for me. He say he seen it in a Latin document, whatever that is. Here it is: here!"

He handed the paper to Sarah who put on her spectacles and peered at it suspiciously.

"*Akermanni et Carucarrii*. Whatever gibberish is this?"

"Latin, didn't I now tell you, gel! And there's the English for it underneath: *Acremen and ploughmen*. And he say that an *akerman* were a man who had an acre o' land let to him while he done work for the lord."

"For the Lord! For the Charch you mean?"

"No, no, no, gel. Not Him up there. Him who say he own the land; the lord o' the manor! Mr. Robertson, he reckon my name were handed down from them folks. What you think o' thet, gel?"

But Sarah didn't seem impressed and asked coolly:

"And what did you say to him?"

This was the question that Acky needed.

"I made him laugh, gel. He laugh so much he fare double up over his spade.

" 'Akerman,' I say; 'well, my grandfather and a' them must ha' been some careless, or thet owd lord must ha' been some sly, I reckon. For some'un has been nibbling at my acre good tidily; 'cos all I got left on it now is less than a quarter-acre. And if they build thet new road they're a-talking about, I'll hardly have enough land to grow a bit o' mint for ma sauce.' "

"Sauce! You got a rare lot too much o' that already," said Sarah. "But you better be some careful how you talk to thet schoolmaster. He'll have you in atween the covers of a book afore you know what's happened to you. And how will you fare then? You'd be in a right pickle then!"

"Oh, I wouldn't mind about thet! I allus got a fancy to git my name into the papers. And a good name it is, too; like he say."

But Acky's talk with the schoolmaster made him return to a problem that had taken up most of his real thinking during the greater part of his life: how to get a fair piece of land that he could work on and call his own. That was the mainspring of all his striving: his keeping of pigs, his poaching, his grubbing around doing small jobs—the whole of his saving; it was to get enough money to rent or buy a piece of land that he could farm as his own. Now that he had retired he had more time for thinking; and this small piece of land was always the bed and bottom of his thoughts. He'd often looked at the Common outside his own *yard*, or allotment, with a speculative eye. But there was, he well knew, little chance of an answer to his problem in that direction.

Then one Sunday morning he was walking across the Common when he noticed a party by the old mound or tumulus that was near the centre of the stretch of heathland. They were bending over something; from a distance it looked as if two or three of them were digging. Acky first got Bundler to heel and then strolled across. As he approached he recognized the schoolmaster who called out:

"We've got a spare spade here, Mr. Flatt, if you'd care to feel the handle of it."

But Acky was too wily a bird to be taken in by such an invitation, and he answered cheerfully:

"Thank you kindly, Mr. Robertson; but my owd back don't fare to be what it should, this morning." And after he'd watched the three men and a girl digging away for a few minutes he called Bundler and continued on his walk.

That same afternoon Acky was standing at the gate of his cottage at the other end of the Common when Tom Downey passed. He was driving the Firtree cattle down to the marshes. He stopped and asked:

"What are they a-doing on up there on the Common, Acky? They're a-digging up there as if they meant it."

"That they are!" Acky agreed. "After history, so they tell me, Tom—to see if they cin find ruins or suthen."

"Ruins! Thet's a rum thing to go a-diggin' for," Tom Downey grunted, as he prodded one of the heifers. "If they want some diggin' I got a tidy piece of ma owd yard that I haven't started on yet. Thet could do with some diggin'!"

Acky nodded; but when Tom Downey had gone, a certain light came into his eye. Tom wasn't a beetle-head after all: there was some good sound sense in what he was saying. What a waste of good digging energy to go spending it all on ruins! He went into his allotment at the side of his house. A turn round his *owd yard*, as he called it, helped him in his thinking. He walked slowly to the bottom, fingering one of his ear-rings and looking thoughtfully out on to the bit of Common on the other side of the fence. Then he suddenly hurried into the house; put on his jacket and walked purposefully up to the village.

His broad face was shining when he came to the cottage of old Silas Crosby who had once been a horseman with him on Firtree Farm. Silas was sitting outside peeling a few potatoes ready for his evening meal. He was a tricky old man, but Acky went straight to the point:

"You recollect thet owd coin you turn up, Silas?"

"Which 'un were that?" the old man asked, looking at Acky shrewdly. "I turned up a rare lot o' coins in my time, I have."

"You know the one I mean. This 'un were some owd—all wore up. You shew it me. On Schol'us Walk you plough it up, weren't it?"

The old man dropped the potato-knife into the bowl:

"Now that were a whoolly fine coin that were. Worth a lot more'n those ear-rings o' yourn, I reckon, Acky."

"I don't doubt—but I thought you'd recollect it, Silas. You don't fare to have it somewhere about, do you?"

"Maybe I have, maybe I haven't," the old man answered, with a sly look at Acky before picking up his knife and turning his attention to the bowl of potatoes.

But Acky was man enough for old Silas; and it wasn't long before the coin was in his pocket and he was walking straight over to call on the schoolmaster. As it happened he was working in his garden.

" 'Evening, sir," Acky called out. "I brought something maybe you'd like to have a look at."

He produced the coin, and immediately the schoolmaster leaned his hoe against the fence: "This is interesting. Very interesting, indeed," he said quickly. "Where did you get it from, Mr. Flatt?"

"Picked it up the day afore yesterday on that bit o' Common ahind my own yard. A bit o' ground were disturbed like. Bundler, ma owd dog, must ha' scrabbled it up."

Acky told his story without a blink. But in any case, the schoolmaster was too interested in the coin to pay much attention to Acky.

"If I'm not mistaken this is a second-century Roman coin. Do you mind if I keep it a day or two to get this confirmed?"

"Keep it! Keep it, you," Acky said generously, "until you get it properly fixed. I know you'll be looking arter it. Maybe there's some more where this 'un came from."

Acky went home feeling very pleased with himself. So far his scheme had gone well; but he'd told Sarah very little about it. But she knew his views: it was a shame not to make use of that bit of Common behind the cottage. He'd had his eye on it for some time; only he dare not move his fence forward an inch to take in any of the land. He knew he'd have the whole pack of village lawyers down on him like a shower of acorns on a windy day in October. And Joe Easy, the parish clerk, would be at the head of them. The time he planted a few gooseberry bushes on the wrong side of the fence, they were after him as though he had committed some great crime.

The Coin

"Gooseberries on the Common this year, and gooseberries in your own yard the next, Acky!" Joe Easy had lectured him. "We weren't born yesterday, bor. And most of us have got something else between our ears asides stuffin'."

But, thought Acky, this here looked a more promising scheme altogether; and it would give him a great lift to get round Joe Easy and all the other lawyers.

The following week-end a digging party turned up in full strength to explore the piece of Common where Acky was supposed to have found the coin. He was in tremendous spirits.

"Come to the window, gel," he told Sarah, after he'd explained a little of what was happening. "Do you see that 'un with the glasses? He don't fare to look a likely one, do he? But you wait! He can handle a wheelbarrow half-tidy once he gits a-going."

By Sunday evening the piece of Common had been cultivated as well as if had been done by a pair of horses; and Acky was rubbing his hands at the success of his plan. Although the digging party had found nothing, the schoolmaster didn't seem very much put out.

"We'll be back next week-end. We need patience for this job, Mr. Flatt."

"We whoolly do, Mr. Robertson," Acky agreed. Then he added: "Don't you think we'd better have a bit o' nettin' put round where you been a-digging; a fence of some sort. That trench there . . . it'll be kinda dangerous in the dark. Now I got a bit of spare wire here. I shouldn't mind . . ."

"Yes, yes," Mr. Robertson said, "you do that. That's an excellent idea. I'll fix it with the parish council. There'll be no trouble at all."

That was good enough for Acky. Within a couple of days

there was a neat wire fence around the bit of Common, neater in fact than he had round his own chicken-run.

The digging party started early on the following Saturday morning. Acky didn't interfere. He settled down to smoke a pipe by his back door. He calculated that they would have covered most of the piece by the evening; and then, having found nothing, they would pack up their tools; and it was unlikely that they'd ever return. As he enjoyed the sun and kept half an eye on the diggers, Acky went through his plan again: he'd let a few weeks go by then he'd level off the ground; and in the spring he'd sow a handful or two of oats. In the following year he'd maybe give it a trial with a bit of sugar-beet. That would give him a start. He'd fix Joe Easy and his gang this time. He had thought out what he was going to tell him, and quietly rehearsed it:

"This here is a historical piece of land, Joe; and that fence has got to stay up. We got to be some careful with this land while those clever fellers are a-thinking what they're going to do about it. And the best way to look after it and keep it private like is to have something a-growing on it."

Acky had it all beautifully set out. He could see the wilderness blossoming coins; but not the sort that fool the schoolmaster was looking for. The future opened up for him. He'd take a farm and soon Fenhall would be too small to hold him.

His castle-building was disturbed by a shout from the Common. Mrs. Robertson was waving her arms about as though a bull had got loose in the yard; and the spectacled chap was hopping about like a sparrow after a thaw. The schoolmaster was down in a trench; and it was plain that he had found something. Acky hurried across to find out the cause of the excitement. All he could see was a lot of black earth and what looked like a charred bit of an old tree stump.

In a short time the diggers uncovered a considerable area

near the post. The digging revealed some charred and rounded stones, pieces of pottery and three more stumps similar to the one already uncovered. Acky watched gloomily and stayed long enough to hear Mr. Robertson's opinion that they had come across the site of an early British settlement.

"Early British conglomification!" Acky muttered disgustedly as he got back to the cottage. "It's all them books thet school-master's been a-reading; must be, to git ideas like that! Well, that's cooked our little scheme, gel. We got as much chance now o' growing anything on that bit o' land as the man in the moon's got o' raising cabbages."

For a couple of days Acky couldn't bear to look at the piece of Common. But one morning he was surprised by a big car full of people turning up and asking for the site of the excavations. Later that morning two more cars arrived. Soon there were reporters and camera-men and two experts from London roaming all over the patch.

As Acky stood watching from his back window his eyes lit up once more as he fingered one of his ear-rings:

"Why! I got it, gel! Can't you see, we're becoming famous. Who's got that tea-urn they used to have at the Women's Institute? Hold on while I go after it. And you git all the kittles a-boiling; and hunt up a piece o' flannin to wrop the tea in. We're going into the caff business, gel. Fivepence a cup, it'll be—the same as on the railway. And it'll be better tea than the brew you get with them. The water out here fare to have a lot more body in it to start with."

Before the morning was out Acky and Sarah were serving cups of tea as fast as they could hand them out of the window.

"We'll have to lay in the stocks, gel. I hear that bloke with the beard say it's an important find, if you can fathom the meaning o' that. But we can expect some more wisitors. Not so much milk in the cups, gel. They don't give you quarter o' that on the railway."

Within a few weeks the tea business was thriving; and Acky had appointed himself more or less "official" guide to the excavations; and he was talking about Ancient Britons as familiarly and as knowledgeably as if they'd been his neighbours for most of his life. The only wrong note was the schoolmaster who would keep returning to the coin, and worrying over it like a dog over a bone that wouldn't yield him its marrow.

"I can't understand it," he said. "What is a Roman coin of the second century doing in such an early settlement as this? And on its own! There's not a sign of anything else Roman. It's a complete mystery."

But Acky reassured him blandly:

"Oh, don't you worry about that, Mr. Robertson. Them Romans were a sociable lot, you ma' depend. Seemingly, one o' them dropped that coin while he was out a-wisiting. But you don't want to fret about that, sir. Strange things have been happening in Fenhall, ever since I can recollect; and some stranger things were a-going on when them Romans were about. A rare lot o' rum 'uns those Romans were, you ma' depend."

3

The Mattress

When Acky spent a night at home he usually sat by the open hearth of their thatched cottage, quietly smoking his pipe and brooding about one thing and another; while Sarah sat opposite him busily knitting for one or other of their many grandchildren. And Acky, who found it hard to lie down with his own thoughts for more than an hour, often sought a change by gently prodding Sarah into talk. Sarah was slightly deaf; and this evening he chaffed her by telling her:

"O' course, you didn't hear me when I ax you about darning ma socks. But when you come to it, you ain't got time for nawthen bar all thet knitting you do for the babies. But I suppose it's this gineration gap they're on about: the young 'uns are a-climbing all over the old 'uns' backs."

"I hear you," Sarah answered coolly; "and you don't want to go ahid about thet little job. I'll see to it. But I can tell you this: there's one job *you* ought to see to, and that right quick!"

"What's thet?" Acky asked with a yawn, guessing what was coming.

"To put thet money o' yourn into the bank. No money is safe unless it's in the bank."

"Safe!" Acky laughed. "There are safer places than banks. If anyone comes along o' nights and can git you off that owd mattress when you're not wanting to shift, he's welcome to have all the money that's hid up in it, and a half-crown out o' ma pocket as well, jus' for doing what I've never been able to do in ma life."

"But look at the interest you'd git in the bank."

"Interest; what good would thet be? No, Sarah, you got it wrong about the bank. As soon as I'd pay ma money in there, those income-tax billies would be on to it like a lot of long dogs on to a silly hare. And where would the interest be then? This little bit is nawthen to do with them blokes. This is winnings, gel. Winnings! And if you don't start a-slimming, it's right safe where it is. I'll back thet owd mattress agin the Bank of England, any day of the week."

But Sarah had another reason for wishing he'd put his money in the bank. For when the fancy took him Acky tore up the side of the mattress, took out all his notes and spent an evening ironing them flat with the smoothing iron. And when Sarah complained about the feathers that were scattered about the bedroom, he said;

"If you didn't keep a-tossing and a-turning so much in the bed, gel, I'd ha' no cause to do this. If you laid flat and tidy like a neat lil' owd body should, these here notes would be as crisp as when I sewed them in. Instead o'—but see here, they're all screwed up like a lot o' toffee-papers. It don't fare to be right for notes of the realm to be treated like that!"

"Notes of the realm! I don't know what you mean by that! All I know is, with your ideas about hiding up your money in a feather mattress I got more work in this tiddy lil' cottage than I had when I was working for Mrs. Vesey up at the Grange."

"Talk, gel, jus' talk," Acky grunted. "You're a-livin' in the past. Thet was forty year since; and owd Mrs. Vesey and her daughter, the painting woman, don't signify. What have they got to do with this here?"

"Nawthen at all," Sarah admitted. "But I know this: if owd Mrs. Vesey were alive, she'd be the one to talk some sense into that hid o' yours. Safe she would! She done it so many times afore."

"Her! She were an owd harridan. Besides, I were young then and green; and I listened to what the owd gel told me. I were nothing else but a back'us boy then. But I liked the painting woman. Elaine they called her, weren't it? She were different. I would ha' got the top apple off the tree for her."

Sarah sighed and let her knitting fall into her lap. She looked up at the oil painting that hung on the wall opposite the fireplace.

"Yes, she were a fine woman, and a good painter, too. To think that she painted you as an angel in that picture there, Acky Flatt. If she only knew what you were a-turning out to be!"

"Stop your puttering, gel. I told you I were young then, and kind o' sensitive."

Acky got up and took the picture down and brought it into the light. It showed a group of figures standing round a central one on a classical portico: "Don't you think I made a tiddy angel, gel?" Acky laughed. "Just you look on it."

But Sarah said sharply: "Be careful with it now!" Then to rile him: "An angel! And thet's Tom Blowers who is right opposite you on the other side of the picture. Poor owd Tom's gone. I reckon he's a real angel now. But you, Acky Flatt, you're further from being an angel than Boxing Day is from next Christmas!"

When Sarah got on to the picture Acky either shut up or went into the garden. The picture was his sore place; and he had often suggested to her that she should get rid of it—sell it or give it to one of their children. But Sarah clung to it as the one thing in the cottage which she valued. It was also her best and sharpest weapon against Acky. As long as she could point to the picture and tell him: "There you are up there like

Miss Elaine painted you, an angel all smiling and innocent; but when you come to it you're wuss'n the Owd Nick hisself"—as long as she could tell him this, she knew she could shame him into taking his pipe into the garden, leaving her the hearth to enjoy herself in peace. And between Acky's money and Sarah's picture it looked as though the hearth would never see them smiling and benevolent on each side of it, like a pair of old, good-natured china dogs; an old couple content to let the world pass them by almost without notice. But whether they thought much about the world or not, it didn't much matter: the world, it seemed, was on the point of thinking about them.

It was late autumn and as usual the village boys were experimenting with fire and fireworks. As usual, too, they set fire to the gorse on the Common. But this year, by a lack of his usual caution, Acky was not about when it happened. He had gone over to Ditton to visit a cousin who was sick. When he came back he found that the Common was well alight to within twenty yards of their door. But, worse still, the wind was right behind the fire, driving showers of sparks all over the thatch like chaff at a threshing. Of course, Sarah was inside, and in spite of the noise and the shouting she knew about as much of what was happening as if she had been sitting quietly knitting on the moon.

Acky rushed into the living-room shouting:

"The Common's ablaze, gel; and the thatch will be alight in no time! We'll hev to get the stuff out right quick!"

Then he darted out and shouted into the darkness: "Ring the fire brigade, you rascals!" The rascals, however, had fled. But, luckily, Jim Burrows happened to be passing from Ditton way on his bike. He saw what was happening and he was soon in the telephone-box ringing up the police, the doctors, the ambulance and half the fire brigades in the country.

While all this was going on Acky and Sarah had started getting their belongings out of the cottage. One of the first things Sarah made for was her picture.

"You can leave thet," Acky grunted, as he carried the mattress down the stairs. "Don't waste time bothering about thet! There's the pots and pans and all the rest of the important stuff to get out, gel."

By this time the roof of the cottage was alight and smoke was pouring from one corner of the thatch like the beginning of a rick-fire. Fortunately, though, there was more smoke than flame, as there had been a shower of rain that morning, and the thatch was still damp under the surface. A dozen or so neighbours soon came flocking across to help; and they got most of the furniture out and stacked it at the side of the cottage, well away from the bank of gorse and bracken that was still burning fitfully. Then the first fire brigade turned up and panicked round for water until they got a long hose down to Firtree pond. By the time the pump was properly working, a corner of the thatch was well ablaze; but with two hoses going they soon sprinkled that down. Then another fire brigade turned up from Stowport way, an eager gang of men who quickly had a spurt of water breaking one of the upstairs windows and pouring into the front bedroom.

Standing by his mattress Acky shouted out:

"Hold hard there, togither! Hold hard! You'll wash the lil' owd place right away if you're not some careful!"

But things were getting right out of hand as far as Acky and Sarah were concerned. Firemen and policemen and neighbours were rushing about like children at a firework display; and to Sarah and Acky it seemed that they had already lost their cottage and all their belongings which had been taken over by the fire quenchers. Sarah had placed her picture on the old wash-

C

ing-stand, and she was wringing her hands at the damage they seemed to be causing. Then a new gang of firemen began to shift the furniture farther away in case, as they said, the flames started up again. Two of them made for the mattress; and since Acky had already shouted himself hoarse without anyone taking notice, he decided the time had come for a bit of action. So when the firemen bent down to take the mattress more or less forcibly away from him, Acky flopped down on it in a faint that the best "dying" actor on the stage wouldn't have been ashamed of.

"It were the heat," Acky—who had never fainted in his life —explained afterwards, "and all that smoke and fumes; and those chaps a-rushing about and swearing. It were too much for me."

When he decided it was time for him to come round, he saw Sarah leaning over him, more concerned than he ever imagined she could be. She had even forgotten her picture in her anxiety. The fire, he noticed, had been put right out, and the whole scene was now lit up by the headlights of the two fire-engines.

As soon as Acky was sitting up Sarah went across to see what was happening to her picture. For a group of men were standing around it, and she was just in time to retrieve it from a tall man in tweeds. He had picked it up meaning to take it to one of the headlights to examine it more closely.

The damage to the cottage was slight. More harm came to it from the water as Acky had forecast; and it was much too damp for them to return to it that night. So they covered up all the furniture with a big barn-tilt; and went over to Jim Burrows's place and decided to sleep there for the night. As they were starting Jim said to Acky:

"You don't want to bring thet mattress with you, bor. We got plenty o' spare bedding over at ours."

But Acky answered: "I fare to think I'll kinda take up ma bed and walk. Thank ye, kindly, Jim. I'm 'tracted to this owd mattress; and I'm allus sure of a good night's rest when I'm a-laying on it."

Sarah, too, took her picture with her; and they spent the night in better comfort and in more peace of mind than they could have hoped for earlier in the evening. And in two days' time they were back in their cottage which seemed none the worse except for the bit of burnt thatch, a few stains on the wall and a damp smell which Acky said a good log fire or two would soon chase up the chimney.

The fire, however, had bitten deep into Acky; and at the end of the week, after he'd drawn his pension, he said to Sarah:

"Maybe you're right about thet bank, gel."

" 'Course I'm right. And it took a fire to knock it into thet wooden hid o' yourn. You better rip thet mattress up for the last time, and ease yourself of all thet money."

By the following morning Acky had made up his mind what he was going to do. He put on his best suit; made up his notes into a great parcel with two pieces of cardboard to stiffen it and keep it flat and straight; stuffed the parcel under his jacket and set off to cycle the six miles to the village of Fordham.

"It's like this here," he explained to Sarah before he left. "There's a streetful o' Flatts away over to Fordham. And if I'm not right mistaken there's an Akerman among 'em, too. If I take ma money to the post-office over there, maybe those fly income-tax blokes will get the scent wrong, and we'll be able to fox 'em good-tidily."

When he returned that evening after depositing his savings at Fordham he found Sarah sitting by the table in her best dress and her string of beads she wore only on special occasions.

"Where you going, gel?" he asked quite mystified. "Or is it suthen, some date I forgot?"

She pointed to a piece of paper neatly folded under a cream-jug in front of her.

"I sold my picture," she said quietly; "and that's a cheque if you've niver seen one afore, Acky Flatt."

Acky picked it up: "A cheque! For—for seventy! Seventy pound! for thet bit of picture, gel!" He sat down at the table and poured himself a cup out of the pot of tea Sarah had been celebrating with.

"Yeh," she said, "and it's a right good job I don't think the same about cheques as you do, bor. Dr. Bulley brought the gentleman over to see the picture. I recognized him straight away. He were the one I see looking at the picture the night o' the fire. I knew he were all right since he were with Dr. Bulley."

"Well, my heart alive!" said Acky, as he loosened and took off his collar. "I'm whoolly flabbergasted! But what are you going to do with this cheque here. I can see I'll have to go over to Fordham agin tomorrow."

Sarah, however, took up the cheque and folded it neatly before replacing it under the cream-jug.

"I must hev time to think about that, Acky. Dr. Bulley he say he'll change it for money if I wanted it that way. And I'm not so sure it wouldn't be better like that."

"Did he now? It's up to you to say, gel."

"Yeh, yeh. But you ain't sewed that owd mattress up again, hev you, Acky? I fare to think we'd better leave it yet awhile till I kinda properly made up ma mind."

4

The Shield

Until you had lived in the village of Fenhall for at least a couple of generations you were still a *furriner*; and as a foreigner you were expected to keep to your place. A newcomer to Fenhall must always state his opinion in a very small voice indeed. In fact, it would be much better if he didn't state it at all. For although he couldn't help being seen about the village—after all a man has to live somewhere—the foreigner ought not to be as rash as to make himself heard. This, at least, is what Akerman Flatt thought of Mrs. Horringer who'd shown a strong intention of settling in Peartree Cottage.

Now Mrs. Horringer was a good woman with as much energy as a committee of public workers; and she hadn't been long in Fenhall before she was making herself felt. She got herself a place on the Parish Council, the Mothers' Union, the School Managers; and after she had been in the village for about four years she was elected President of the Women's Institute. As soon as she got to that position she began a drive to tidy up the village and to persuade it to enter the Best Kept Village Competition that was being organized in the county.

When Acky heard this he said: "What's the owd man-woman a-doing on now? She's not been in the village five minutes afore she mun be gitting everybody organized—a-toeing the line like she's the schoolmistress and us togither is a lot o' kids. What's wrong with the place? Fenhall's one o' the best lil' owd villages in Suffolk. What she want cod-wallopin' about to tarn it upside down for to win some owd tin shield? Did you hear she got 'em to pull down thet owd barn just on the road at the corner o' Mr. Tomlin's meadow? The old place weren't much to look at; but it would have sarved right well for some'un to keep his pigs in!"

But Sarah was not altogether with him in this. As a member of the Women's Institute her ears had been opened to the glories that would come to Fenhall if the village would only pull itself together and spruce itself up.

"It is", Mrs. Horringer had said, sounding a fighting note that had rarely been heard in the parish hall, "one of the prettiest villages in the county. It only wants us to straighten its bonnet and trim the fravelings off its frock, if I may say so."

So while Acky muttered and grumbled about the things they were doing to the village, Sarah sat at the other side of the hearth and lectured him:

"You're a-getting set in your ways, Acky Flatt. You're afraid of anything new. That's the trouble with you! You want us all in Fenhall to go no faster than an owd hodmedod. You want to keep up with the times like the Prisident say; we want to put the village on the map."

"Ha! Now you're talking, gel. You're a-talking some sense. I *am* right afeered of anything new when it's like thet Prisident o' yourn. I'm so afeered I'd run a mile along the Ditton road if I see her a-coming. As for the village, it's a rare owd pity we didn't put the bar up on the gate afore this Mrs. Horringer got here in the first place."

But Acky used something else beside talk, as everyone knew when the tidying-up campaign began in earnest. For though his cottage was right on the edge of the heath, almost on the parish boundary, the enclosure at the side and the back of it—his *owd yard*, as Acky called it—was so much in need of tidying up it would almost be a waste of time for the village to enter the competition unless Acky did something about it. Not that he was a bad gardener: indeed, Akerman Flatt was one of the best gardeners in the parish. But he was also one of the best hoarders. He could not bear to part with anything that was likely to be of remote use to him about the house or his small piece of land: logs of wood, odd scraps of furniture, an old bicycle, a pair of cartwheels, the skeleton of an old cart, some old-fashioned forms turned out of the village school, an old washing-machine he'd once picked up at a sale—so that the side of his yard was filled with what looked like the flotsam of a deserted village. Acky's yard was so spectacular that it had become famous in the neighbourhood.

Therefore Mrs. Horringer could see that it was no use her trying to put pressure on him to clear up his yard. She'd been in the village long enough to know that. Her only hope was to get at him through his wife. For the next few weeks Sarah had more than her share of attention at Institute meetings; and she was soon won round to the organizers' way of thinking. And she promised to talk again to her husband. Sarah started her campaign; and at first Acky turned a broad back to it all; but after she had missed giving him a meal or two he saw he would have to put up at least a show of doing what she wanted him to. He said he'd tidy up his yard, pack most of the odds and ends away; and then set a row of early peas right across the garden to screen the patched-up shed from the roadway. He even helped to straighten up the old boundary stone—which was a few yards on the Ditton side of his cottage and had tilted over perilously. So far so good; Mrs. Horringer was very pleased and congratulated Sarah at the next meeting of the Institute; and Sarah beamed like a midday sun. But Mrs. Horringer added:

"There's still the matter of the bedsteads in the fence, Mrs. Flatt. If you can get your husband to take those out and hide them somewhere, I do believe we have a good chance of winning this Shield."

But Acky had already refused to do anything about the bedsteads, and Sarah had given up trying to persuade him. For he had told her in a voice she recognized as carrying the last words on the subject:

"Don't you ask me to rip those owd bedsteads out ma' fence, gel. I think a lot on 'em, and you know it! I wouldn't shift 'em for a bus-load o' Presidents. Whoi! There's half the history o' the Flatt family in them bedsteads. We can't use 'em lightly, gel. We got to treat 'em with some respect. There's the one with the painted picture on it: that's the one ma Uncle Ephraim laid on for five year with his artheritis, afore he went to a better place. Then there's the one with the brass knobs. That's ma grandfather's wedding bed; and the plain solid one—that's the one I were born on, gel; and if the old slats hadn't kinda deciduated we'd be using on it now."

The bedsteads, therefore, stayed in the fence; and the Women's Institute hoped that by the time of the judging of the competition there would be enough growth in the hedge to cover up at least some of its worst features. The hope was short-lived; for as time went on, it became clear that the brass and the curlecues on Acky's bedsteads were not going to be subdued even by the generous growth of a particularly lavish June —and June was the month of judging.

No one knew on which day the judges would be coming out; and as there were so many villages to be visited, no one could begin to guess. The Women's Institute organized their annual

June outing to the seaside, as usual, without any misgivings. They would leave things as tidy as they could, and if the judges arrived on the day they were away it would make no difference.

But no one really believed the judges would come out on the 22nd June, the fine day the Institute chose for their outing. As soon as the two buses had left with the women, all marshalled by Mrs. Horringer and her committee, Acky took his pipe and sat on the seat at the front of his cottage.

"It's suthen to have a bit o' peace," he said to himself. "No women a-puttering about the place. It will do some on 'em good to set up there on the beach and put up with a bit o' real competition from the sea-gulls."

Yet by the time he had smoked a couple of pipes, had a look at his row of peas and got himself a bite to eat, Acky found that the morning was tending to drag. So he decided to get out his bike and pedal over to Fordham. He wanted to see Fred Partridge about a young pig he had for sale; and maybe he'd call in the Ditton *Rose* on the way back for a pint and bit of news.

The weather, after a chill start, got much warmer; and Acky, finding cycling thirsty work, changed his mind and went straight to the *Rose* for some refreshment. The kitchen bar of the pub was half full of Ditton men who had called in for a drink, but chiefly to find out what was happening in the village that morning. Two strangers, they said, were walking about looking at Ditton as if they were figuring to buy it. Acky came in just as the landlord was clearing up the mystery:

"Don't you know! They're two o' the judges for the Best Trimmed Village Competition. They're coming back here for something to eat before they do the next village, Fenhall most likely."

"Ooh, ah! I reckon you hit it, Parcy. I been dinning my hid to recollect where I see that bloke in the overcoat afore."

"What he want an owd duffel-coat on in this weather? It ain't cold."

"Oh, that's to show he's a judge. Don't you understand? The other one has growed himself a beard for the same parpose."

Acky stood listening quietly sipping his pint. But then they turned to him and began to chip him about his village entering for the Shield. He was a bit angry; all that was nothing to do with him. He'd heard enough about this Shield to last him a lifetime. And why did they want to bring it up on the one day there was a chance of a bit of peace? Naturally, Acky didn't show he was annoyed: he just sat and looked as impassive as usual. But when Percy Pearce the landlord said to him with a sly wink at the others:

"I reckon, Acky, with that old yard and that fence o' yours, you're about the best support Ditton could have in this competition. You certainly put Fenhall right out o' the running."

Acky now came a little way out of his shell:

"All right, Percy," he said. "You allus know which side o' the hedge the owd hin is a-going to lay the egg. But I tell you one thing: Ditton isn't going to win this Shield." There was a silence after he'd said this, long enough for Acky to wonder what had made him open his mouth at all.

"Who is then?" the landlord asked.

"Whoi, Fenhall's going to win it!"

There was a loud cackle of laughter with everyone except Acky joining in. Acky took an old tin tobacco box out of his pocket, and when the laughter had died down he placed it on the counter with a bang:

"I'll take anybody for an even pound that Fenhall will win the competition!"

Four of the Ditton men came forward immediately and handed over their notes to the landlord, while Acky carefully counted four out of his tin box to cover them.

When Acky was back on the road a few minutes later he said to himself: "Blast 'em all! What made me get mixed up in that? Now I got to do suthen right quick afore the judges have finished their dinner." But a plan formed itself as he cycled quickly along the road back to Fenhall. As soon as he came to his cottage he propped his bike against the gate and hurried inside. A minute or two later he came out again with a pick and shovel. Acky worked hard for an hour, keeping a sharp eye on the road he had just travelled. Fortunately, no traffic of any account passed, and no one saw what he was doing. But just after he had finished his job he saw a car away in the distance approaching from the Ditton direction. He took his tools inside, and hid behind the thickest part of his fence. The car slowed up and the two judges got out.

"Ah, here's the boundary stone. Fine! Someone has even cleaned it up!"

"I wonder which village did that: Ditton or Fenhall?" asked the judge with the beard. "But look at this fence! Atrocious! and the bedsteads! Some awkward customer won't co-operate, evidently. Too bad; but we'll have to put it down against them —and pretty heavily at that."

As soon as the judges had gone, Acky went indoors, washed his hands and lay down on his bed to recover from his exertions.

That evening he happened to be crossing the Knoll up in the village just as the Institute coaches returned from the outing. As the women got out Acky told them, as if he'd been one of the organizers:

"We been judged, ladies! We been judged; and I fare to think we ha'n't been found a-wanting."

Of course the women were angry, remembering Acky's obstinacy; and Sarah showed him the length of her tongue as they walked across the heath to their cottage. But Acky said mildly: "Don't jaw me, gel. Write it down on a postcard and I can read it in the marning."

That night, however, he left his bed in the small hours while Sarah, who was still half asleep, grumbled about his taking up his old poaching ways again. He went downstairs and, taking his pick and shovel, quietly returned the boundary stone to its rightful place near his cottage, muttering to himself as he did so: "It's better thar. I reckon I couldn't sleep in Ditton one night without getting a horrible nightmare!"

About a month later Fenhall heard the surprising but heartening news that they had won the Shield in the county Best Kept Village Competition. As soon as the news came through Acky received a visit from the President. She was loud in her thanks for the way he had co-operated, even though— as she said—she had no idea how he'd cleaned up his place so quickly at the last moment. But after listening to her benevolently Acky told her, his head on one side and his words as smooth in his mouth as butter:

"You see, ma'am, when I come to it I couldn't let the village down. I'm a kinda rough diamond as you moight say; but I got a soft heart—as my Sarah will tell you. And there's nawthen I wouldn't do for Fenhall. But if you'll excuse me now, ma'am, I now got to take a turn over to Ditton. They mun be some disappointed over thar; and I reckon it would be right neighbourly to consolate with them togither for an hour or two."

5

Light from Under a Very Dark Bushel

Sarah was an expert at making patchwork quilts. Even Acky admired her handwork; and although he didn't praise her to her face he used to boast to his friends that his "Sarah were a maaster-hand with the needle". But it was different when Mrs. Horringer saw one of Sarah's quilts and immediately "took her up". She persuaded her to give a demonstration at the Institute. The demonstration was so successful Sarah was soon being taken round to other Institutes to show her skill. And her engagements came so fast that she was often out two evenings in the week. This didn't please Acky; and it brought the old conflict with Mrs. Horringer out into the open again.

"You're making a reg'lar pastime o' this now, ain't you, gel? You've gone and let this Prisident butter you up, and now you're a-traipsing round the countryside like some owd travelling-woman. You scarce got time to mend ma socks. I reckon the W.I. wasn't set up for such capers as this!"

But Sarah turned her deaf ear to Acky's moaning; and it is very likely that as her visits to neighbouring Institutes became fewer and fewer the whole business of the quilts would have been forgotten. About this time, however, Mrs. Horringer received the programme of the two-day county show that was to be held in June. The Institutes, it appeared, were going to put on a "live exhibition" of rural crafts. Immediately the President thought of Sarah's special quilt-making; and she was

determined that she would be there in the Institute tent showing all the bigger branches what a small and unknown Institute
like Fenhall could do when it came to real skill in country
crafts. But the President counted without Acky; for when he
heard about the proposal that Sarah should demonstrate her
quilt-making, he became stubborn and refused to shift an inch.

"You can tell that Prisident of yourn I'm not going to play.
Two days at the county show for certain; and most likely the
day afore as well—to set the tent up. Who do you think is
a-going to feed the animals?"

"There's only one animal you're a-thinkin' on, Akerman
Flatt," Sarah said.

"Now look here, gel," he said firmly, as though to close the
subject; "you can put it all out o' your mind. These patchwork
quilts ha' gone to the President's head. She dreams about 'em
o' nights; but she fare to be right out o' bed over this. You
don't want to be a-setting up there two days in a drafty owd
tent. It would bring you in nawthen except a bad attack o'
your rheumatics."

Sarah knew that there was no use in arguing with Acky
when he was in this mood. Therefore at the next meeting of the
Institute committee she told the President: "I'm sorry I won't
be able to come to the county show, Mrs. Horringer. Acky is
putting on his parts again, and he says he won't co-operate."

Now, as you know, this Mrs. Horringer was a determined
woman; and she decided there and then to go down and persuade Acky herself. It was a sunny evening and she walked
down to the cottage with Sarah. Acky was sitting outside
admiring a new pair of boots he had just put on in order to
break them in before wearing them away from the house.

"Why, Mr. Flatt," Mrs. Horringer greeted him brightly,
"you're wearing a new pair of boots!"

"Yeh, I know: I put 'em there!"

After that beginning Mrs. Horringer knew that she would have a hard task; and, indeed, Acky was like a rock.

A little later he retreated indoors, lit his pipe and said the final word: "She done too much dimonstrating. She'll be better off at hoom." And he put up such a screen of shag-tobacco smoke that Mrs. Horringer was soon coughing her way towards the door. But just as she opened it and the extra light lit up the gloom of the living-room, she noticed something hanging on the opposite wall. It was an old corn-dolly expertly plaited in wheatstraw.

"What a beautiful thing," said Mrs. Horringer, coming back into the room; "a remarkably fine specimen! Who made it, Mrs. Flatt?"

"Oh, that some o' Acky's work. He learned it from his grandad when he were a tiddy little boy."

"Is that right, Mr. Flatt? You've certainly been hiding your light under a bushel."

"Have I?" Acky said gloomily. "And I now know what you're going to say. But don't say it, ma'am! You won't git me in no tent a-plaiting of corn-dollies. No, ma'am. You can ask old Silas Crosby. He can do them better'n me; and he'll dimonstrate for you. You go down and see him. He's all alive and kickin'. It were only yesterday he was up here a-hollering that I'd shot one of his hins, up on the Common there. As if Akerman Flatt would do sich a thing!"

Mrs. Horringer went off a little disappointed that she had not been able to influence Acky. But the corn-dolly was so interesting that she decided to do what he had suggested and call on old Mr. Crosby. Silas Crosby was a widower who lived by himself in a cottage near Jim Burrows, a couple of hundred yards from the Flatts. Mrs. Horringer found him at home; but as soon as she mentioned Acky Flatt, the old man raised his stick and beat a tattoo on the floor in his anger.

"That Acky! I'll have him pulled. I'll have the law on him yet! He goes out a-poaching on the Common with a gun; and only the other night he shot one of ma best hins. It had taken to straying up there reg'lar. I find some of the feathers. But I can't rightly prove it; and he say he don't know nawthen about it. The rascal! I'll have him pulled, if it's the last thing I have breath for."

Mrs. Horringer waited until the spate of words had flowed past her; and then she asked him about his skill at making corn-dollies. The old man shook his head: "Made dozens when I were younger. But you see ma hands now," he held them out, all gnarled and knotted with arthritis, "there's little I can do with 'em now." Mrs. Horringer sympathized with him and did not press him any further. But just as she was leaving an idea came to her, and she asked:

"Are you sure, Mr. Crosby, that Acky Flatt still goes out poaching on the Common?"

"Sure!" the old man said, raising his stick once more. "He's niver given it up. He spends more time out on the Common and thereabouts at night than he spends in his own bed. He got poaching in his blood; and he'll snaffle anything with feathers on it. It's second nature to him. The willain!"

As Mrs. Horringer walked away from the old man's cottage she decided to return immediately to the Flatts. She had the interests of the Women's Institute at heart and to further these she was prepared not to be too fastidious, and to do things she would never dream of doing on her own behalf. So this time she went into battle against Acky with vigour and with few misgivings.

"Ah, Mr. Flatt," she said, as Acky opened the door. "I saw

Mr. Crosby, and I'm afraid he can't help me with the corn-dollies. No, no, no! I'm not going to bother you again with that business. I want to ask your opinion about another matter. If what Mr. Crosby tells me is true, there's a lot of poaching going on around the Common. Now I think we ought to do something about that. We shouldn't like to see the village get a bad reputation; and perhaps innocent people like yourself come under suspicion. I've a mind to get the policeman over from Ditton, just to have a walk round. I'd like your opinion first. I should hate to see the husband of one of our members (it could well happen, you know!) being taken to court for a poaching offence. It would get the Institute such a terribly bad name."

Acky looked at her, his small eyes moving restlessly as he fingered one of his ear-rings:

"I think you'd better come in again, ma'am. Us together better have a little talk about this poaching."

Before they had spent a couple of minutes in preliminary skirmishing, Acky had sensed the "lie of the land": he saw that Mrs. Horringer had more cunning than he'd credited her with. He therefore did a very skilful and quite unashamed bit of back-pedalling; and before the President left the cottage the second time he assured her like an old friend:

"Don't you worry, ma'am. I'll make one o' them old corn-babbies for you—maybe I can persuade my Sarah to have a dimonstration together—if you can find a tent big enough for the two of us to set in."

Mrs. Horringer left the cottage in high spirits. Fenhall W.I. was little known outside its immediate neighbourhood; but if she could keep Acky to his word, it would soon be known all over the county. As for Acky, as soon as she had gone he sat down and pondered, nodding his head slowly:

"D'you know, gel, thet Prisident o' yourn hasn't been in

the village some long while; but she's beginning to find her way about half-tidy. She's been a-layin' awake at nights a-thinking, you may depend."

Acky was cunning. He knew when to be firm and he knew when to bend; and in this business of the corn-dollies he sensed he would have to be as pliable as a willow-sapling: "It looks as if old Silas has been a-snortin' and a-shootin' of his tongue; and though he can't prove nawthen it would be right awkward if the Ditton policeman were reminded there was ever such a place as Fenhall. There's too many things a-going on at nights to have him up here a-searching."

So without thinking any more about the quarrel with the Women's Institute, Acky visited Thatch Farm and got Mr. Tomlin to give him a few bundles of good wheatstraw. He set to work without delay to make a corn-dolly, "just to keep the Prisident in good heart". And it was soon arranged that Acky and Sarah should attend the county show on both days, demonstrating their separate skills. Acky got Jim Burrows to walk over the Common to feed the pigs, chickens, geese, and so on, while they were to be away; and he made all the other arrangements. But he didn't look forward to the outing very much: sitting in a tent making corn-dollies wasn't his idea of a pastime. But he packed a couple of bottles of beer in his bundles of straw; and he looked forward to retreating behind the tent with one of these to console himself whenever the President or the women got to be more than he could put up with.

On the first day of the show Mrs. Horringer arrived very early at the Flatts' cottage, and packed Sarah and Acky and all their gear into her car.

"You'll enjoy yourself, Mr. Flatt," the President assured Acky as they started off. "It will be an experience, one you've never had before in your life."

"That's some true," Acky said politely; and then under his breath: "And I'll be a right fule if I ever put myself in the way of having it again!"

But once he was installed in the tent, and had unpacked and damped his straw again, and had started work, Acky was soon enjoying himself—especially as the morning wore on, the continuous stream of people who passed through the tent spent most of their time at his corner.

"You see what it is, gel," he boasted to Sarah during a lull, "the quickness of the hand deceive the eye. I'm now a-getting my owd knack. I can do one right well in less than a quarter of an hour."

It was not, however, until the early afternoon that a new prospect opened out for Acky. He was completing a dolly with a very old, five-strand design: it had just come back to him, from the tips of his fingers, you could say—when a middle-aged woman said decisively:

"I'd like to buy that! Do you think ten shillings a reasonable sum to pay for it?"

Now when he heard this Acky nearly fell off his stool. But he covered up his surprise and said as casually as he could:

"I reckon it would be, ma'am. But I doubt I can wrap it up for you. I got no kind o' packing at all."

After that neither Acky's fingers nor his tongue could work fast enough. He sold the dollies as fast as he could make them, but only when the President was not to be seen. If there was someone about he quietly told his customer with a wink and a grin: "Do write your name and address plain on this piece o' paper, and I'll see you get your dolly afore next week's out."

It was only a lack of straw that made him ease off before the end of the day. But as he chatted to the people who viewed his little display he took as many orders as he could; and he finished up with his eyes twinkling. He told Sarah in a whisper as they packed up:

"We're on to suthen, gel! Your Prisident say I been a-hiding my light under a bushel. From now on I reckon I'll make it to shine afar from the roof-tops."

That night, as they were returning home, Acky got Mrs. Horringer to drop him at Tomlin's farm; and the next morning, when she called for him and Sarah, she found him standing by a bale of straw that was nearly as high as himself.

"You're not thinking of taking all that straw, Akerman!" Mrs. Horringer said, as she drew up. "However are we going to get it on to the car?"

"Don't you worry, ma'am. I'll soon stow it away—git you in, Sarah. Do!—and what's left over I'll soon tie on the top with this binder-cord I got handy."

"On the top!"

"Whoi, yeh. It don't weigh heavy. It won't hurt nawthen. And they won't stop us at the gate like they did yesterday. They'll see from all this we're kinda official, and we'll be in that ground afore you can say *Dolly*!"

Acky worked for ten hours that day; but as he told Sarah it was nearly all work for the right firm. For after he had added a few specimens to his display, he sold the rest of the dollies he made—under the counter. His trade was so brisk that he used up his large bundle of straw even before the show finished. But it didn't end before Acky had a long and interesting conversation with a man who had stood watching him closely for half an hour. He turned out to be a buyer from a big London store; and he gave Acky an order for two dozen dollies at a price that was better than he could have dreamed of. When the buyer left, Acky slipped over to the other side of the tent to tell his news to Sarah:

"We're in business again, gel; and I reckon we can keep the owd wolf from the door jus' with owd straw. But there's one thing I'm going to do afore I send one dolly up to Lunnon: I'm going to make a maaster one for that Prisident o' yourn. And I'm going to lace it with ribbon, like I see ma poor owd grandad do for the parson's wedding. That Prisident were a blessin' in disguise: she were just what the village wanted. That's what I allus said was wrong wi' Fenhall: it only wanted a drop o' new blood to make it the finest village in Suffolk."

6.

The Barbecue

It's surprising when you come to think about it, how much the life of the old village revolved round the pig. The pig was sustenance and solace; and sometimes it was also amusement, whether to old men, boys or just babies. But the occasions when it was sustenance, solace and fun—all three together— were very rare indeed. Yet this is what happened when the Fenhall village sports committee, instead of holding the usual fête to raise funds, decided to have a barbecue. The centre of it all was to be a roasted pig; but right at the beginning Acky Flatt asked the basic question: whose pig was it going to be?

You'll see the point of this when you know that the sports committee is one of those combines that buy very cheap and sell very dear. As a matter of fact they buy so cheaply that it is well understood around Fenhall that to ask the committee to pay any money at all is very wrong indeed. Now there is no trouble when it's a matter of a small cockerel for a Christmas draw; but you're on a different plane when you ask someone to give away a whole pig. This wants a bit of considering. Jim Burrows suggested that they tackle Mr. Tomlin at Thatch Farm; but Acky didn't agree:

"No, Jim bor, it mustn't be Mr. Tomlin. I recollect a while back he promised a pig for a quoit match. The pig never turned up. He got better, you see, jus' afore the day!—I'll tell you what I'll do: if you togither agree I'll go up and have a word with young Mr. Copinger."

Acky, you understand, could charm the bird off a tree once he got going. But he wouldn't have got very far if Mr. Copinger wasn't a good-hearted farmer to begin with. As it was, after Acky had told him that he was collecting round the village for the annual effort, as he called it, and he was certain that Mr. Copinger wouldn't want to be left out, and after a bit of talk about a fine crop of barley that Acky admired very much, and how he'd not seen a better one since his father's time, the pig—twenty stone of him at that—was as good as on the spit.

Now Acky had finished on the farm but he was still doing occasional odd jobs; and at this time he was working at the nearby aerodrome which had been taken over by the Americans. He had a job with the boilers, keeping them stoked up and in good order. To hear him talk, though, you'd think he was nothing less than deputy to the controller and commandant of the whole base. Soon after he'd started there he got to know one of the airmen: Top Sergeant Lew Henneker. It was Sergeant Henneker who told Acky when he knew Fenhall was going to have a barbecue:

"You want to do this barbecue in real American style, Acky. I'll tell you what I'll do: I'll get the charcoal for you, cheap; and I'll give you a real genuine sauce to go with that hog meat. I wouldn't tell my own wife what goes into that sauce; but I'll mix it for you. And what's more I'll come along with you and help you cook this pig and serve it up."

The sauce, it appeared, was something very special. It was made from a secret recipe that had belonged to Henneker's grandfather who owned a large cattle-ranch in Texas. Some Mexican Indians who had worked for him had given him the recipe many years before. So when Sergeant Henneker made

his offer, Acky didn't wait to consult the sports committee but
accepted it on the spot.

The barbecue was to be held behind the parish hall where
there was to be a dance and the usual draw as well. On the
previous night, three of the committee with Acky supervising,
dug a large pit, about eighteen inches deep, in which they were
to burn the charcoal. Then they built a small, rough shed
arrangement over the pit in case it came on to rain; and they
next put in stakes to hold the wire-netting—the grill on which
the pork was to be cooked. When the American advised Acky
on the procedure he protested:

"You going to cut the pig up! All Fenhall folk are scheming
to see the pig roasted whole."

"They can, Acky, if they want it that way. But I guess it's
better to eat the pig than just see it roasted in one piece. They
sure wouldn't eat much of it if you did it that way. You'd be
cooking till Christmas. You leave it to me, Acky. We'll do it
American style and there'll be no hitch at all."

But as things turned out a slight hitch did develop on the
following afternoon as they were making their final prepara-
tions for the evening. Just as he was mixing the special sauce,
Sergeant Henneker was called back to the aerodrome. He
was on the aircraft maintenance staff, and a plane that was
on an important mission that evening had developed a fault;
and Sergeant Henneker, it appeared, was the man to put
it right. He swore when he had the message, and said to
Acky:

"Jump in the truck with me, Acky; I'll take you up to the
base. The sauce is finished except for one thing, and you can
fix that yourself. It's in a can in my office. I'll collect it for you
and you can bring it out here. They'll bring you back in this
truck. All you got to do is to pour it into the drum with

what's there, and stir it up well before you heat it. But I guess I'll be back before you get to that stage."

But as soon as the truck reached the gate of the aerodrome it was stopped by the military policemen who told the sergeant he was to go straight to dispersal point where the plane was standing, waiting to taxi to the take-off the moment the fault was cleared. A "jeep" was standing by ready to take him out. So the sergeant just had time to arrange with the policeman to take Acky out to the office to collect the can and then drive him back to Fenhall before he himself was whisked to the other side of the aerodrome.

Acky was now the only bull on the farm. He was in his element: he was the man in charge.

"Now look here togither," he told the rest of the committee when he got back. "We got to do this American style. Sergeant Henneker, he give me all the information. We can make this here a master barbecue. This'll put Fenhall on the map. This pork will smell so good they'll be a-drifting in from Ipsidge way afore the night's out."

And just as Sergeant Henneker had told him he hurried to empty the can into the ten-gallon drum in which they were going to heat the sauce. He next lighted the fire in the pit and stoked it up with the charcoal. Jim Burrows, who had once put in a few years with a butcher, was in charge of cutting up the pig. With his round red face, a white apron and a chef's hat that someone had dug up he looked the right man for the part.

"There's enough hog here to feed an army," he said, as he deftly sliced the pig. "Who you expecting, Acky? The Suffolk Rigiment? If the Fenhall people put half of this away they'll be a-gruntin', and a-sproutin' bristles afore the week's out."

"Don't you worry your fat, Jim. They'll see this hog off.

That they will! Especially with this secret sauce to go with it. I can tell you this is some sauce, a real sauce you can trace back to the Aztecs—whoever they moight be. It's making my mouth water already. Slice it up, Jim. This hog's going to make our name, I reckon."

Everything was well in hand by the time Sergeant Henneker returned; and he was very pleased with Acky's stewardship. He told Acky with a grin:

"I see I can't teach you anything about a hog, Acky. Nohow! You sorta know by instinct."

"I were allus quick to larn," Acky said modestly. "But take a peek at that sauce will you, Sergeant? Afore I put it to heat up. It smell right good to me."

The sergeant walked over to the drum that held the sauce. and with a big spoon he ladled a little out to taste. As he sipped the sauce his face lighted up; then he frowned. He lifted the spoon once more, but this time to smell the sauce. Then he said quietly to Acky:

"Where's the can you took out of my office, Acky? Have you still got it around?"

"What's up? What's up?" Acky asked gruffly, sensing trouble and immediately getting himself ready to bluff his way out of it. "What's up? The can is over there under the table. Just mind your foot there, will you, Jim?"

Sergeant Henneker took up the can and sniffed into it. Then he shook his head and pulled a face:

"Oh boy, oh boy! Acky!" He laughed and it was some time before he recovered. "Acky! You've sure made a master sauce this time. You've durn well laced it with two gallons of finest Jamaica rum!"

In the panic over the delayed take-off the sergeant had omitted to tell Acky that there were two drums in his office: one containing olive oil for the sauce and another rum that he had been storing in readiness for the Independence Day dance that the sergeants' mess was holding. Acky, of course, had taken the wrong one—or maybe it was the right one.

"Well," he said equal, as usual, to the occasion, "it will be a right rum sauce that will go with this pork, and no one can argue about that."

"Sauce!" said the American, who was still laughing, "It'll be strong enough to make that hog pull himself together and walk back home."

"Now look here, Sergeant," Acky said confidentially. "The best drill is to say nawthen. Shut the gate on it, like the owd lady say. They won't know no different. Nobody in Fenhall has ever tasted a Mexican secret sauce afore. Besides, you have rum sauce with your Christmas pudding, and you won't be far out, I reckon, if you have a rum sauce with a nice bit o' pork like this here."

So it was decided that the mistake should be hushed up; and when Sergeant Henneker had tasted the sauce once more after it had been heated up and agreed that it was at least as good as the original, they set themselves to cook the pork.

Now whether it was the smell of the roasting pig or the aroma of the secret sauce that caused it, it would be difficult to tell: but as soon as the cooking got under way the Fenhall folk came out of their houses and made for the back of the parish room as quickly as if they were giving money away there. Acky was there at the centre of the crowd serving the meat and shouting as he did so:

"Roll up! Three bob a portion. The finest meat ever roasted in a barbecue. Fenhall growed, Fenhall dressed and Fenhall cooked; with a real sauce that has never before been made in this country!" and under his breath to Jim Burrows, "nor anywhere else, I doubt! Ladle it out, Jim. We'll convert all those temperance chaps. They'll never preach water is best after tasting this. Wait till we tell 'em. Roll up! All in aid of the playing field."

The pork sold as fast as they could serve it; and the whole evening went without a hitch—until Police Constable Last came over for a stroll from Ditton. He soon sampled the pork and the sauce, and gave his verdict that it was the best he'd ever tasted. But when the pork had all been sold, and the last drop of sauce ladled into the platter, P.C. Last went up to Acky and asked him:

"Did you have a licence to sell that sauce, Acky? There was enough rum in it to float a battleship."

But Acky was not without his answer:

"Rum, Mr. Last? I don't know what you're a-talking about. That was a secret sauce I mun tell you. But look, since you like it so much, there's a bit o' pork and a small can o' sauce for you to take hoom for your missus. Here," he said, producing the can and a small package from under the table. "Do you take it to Mrs. Last with the sports committee's compliments."

Then, a little later, as he saw the constable cycling along the Ditton road:

"The last shall be last, Jim. No doubt he put some time in with the navy to be so sharp as to smell thet rum. There goo our Sunday dinner, Jim; a nice cut it were, too, and a pint o' sauce to wash it down with. The things we do for Fenhall, Jim. The things we do for Fenhall."

7.

The Bird-watchers

The open heath country near the coast attracted many bird enthusiasts, highly equipped professionals as well as the ordinary week-end amateurs. Many of them came to Fenhall heath, and Acky saw them all. He was the man who watched the watchers; and his verdict on them was sharp:

"A-coming all the way from Lunnon jes' to watch lil' owd buds! What do you make o' thet? I reckon there's suthen wrong with their heads. Owd chaps, too, some on 'em: they must be a-coming to their second childhood, sitting in the damp heath and hiding up in the brakes, jes' to spot a little dicky bird you could see six times in a morning if you weren't a-looking for it. Not that I got anything against bird-watching. Bird-watching's all right in its place. If you're working on a field, a-singling beet or suthen like that—it's right interesting to have a breather and see what's a-going on round about. You kinda notice the birds—what time they come and what time they go. D'you know, only last autumn, I were a-watching them rooks; and every afternoon I see 'em returning, and I could set my watch by 'em, the same time every afternoon. You notice lil' things like that. And it's right satisfying to hear and to have a peek at the first cuckoo, weeks afore that clever bloke write to the papers about it. But when it comes to making a job of it, like these fellers are a-doing, I don't hold with it. I don't hold with it all! It's coming to suthen when one half o' the folk is spending their time a-staring into that lil' owd box they got in the corner, their eyes fare goggling at the pictures; and the other half is gitting their toes cold a-watching little birds. Only the other day two men came down the heath in a car that were a'most as big as this house. But, look! They two got as excited as schoolboys because they see a bittern and then an avocet; and as you may well know, both on these buds are about as rare as sparrows round here. But there they were a-chattering and taking notes and photographs like they seen the phoenix itself!"

Yet a year or two ago, something happened that made Acky change his views about bird-watching altogether. He was digging in the garden part of his *owd yard* when he noticed a bird in the hawthorn bush at the bottom. There was something about this bird that made him lean on his spade and keep very still. It was starting to build its nest, and it looked like a blackbird, the male bird with its unmistakable orange bill. But its wings and most of its body were perfectly white: a white blackbird! "Now this is suthen!" Acky muttered to himself. He watched the brown plump female join the bird; saw them potter for a moment or two and then fly off together. A white blackbird, and no mistake! Acky dug his spade into the soil and went indoors to tell Sarah that she would have to keep her old cyprus cat in the house for a day or two. He didn't want it prowling about at the bottom of the garden, frightening off the rare birds that were building a nest there.

Now in Fenhall, as in most small villages, there is a kind of permanent competition. It goes on day in, day out; year in year out without a stop. And though no one ever talks about it, it's more of a pastime than the football pools. Someone wins it nearly every day; but the winner gets no prize except the distinction of being *fust with the news*. Now you'd have thought that Acky Flatt would have taken the floor at the *Plough* that very evening because he'd a bit of news that was rare, and worth immediate telling. But he made no mention of the white bird: he didn't describe it even to Sarah. He was too wily to cry out roast meat. Sarah used to provoke him oftentimes:

"What are you a-thinking on now, Acky Flatt? Cooking up some scheme again. I can niver get to the bottom o' you. You're as deep as Snape River."

Acky rarely talked more than he had to. *Quietness is best*, is the proverb he would have blazoned on his coat-of-arms if he'd had one.

For as soon as Acky saw the white blackbird building its nest at the bottom of the garden, he said to himself: "They say a white pheasant, a white cat or a white horse is lucky. I reckon a white blackbird could be luckier than them all, if I could only see how to start the luck a-running." He observed the birds hatching out their four eggs, putting in more time than any bird-watcher in East Anglia; but he knew enough about birds and animals not to expect any of the young ones to be coloured like the parent. He decided that the best he could do was to let the birds alone to bring up their family quietly, without fuss. The parents would then be almost certain to build on the same spot in the spring of the following year.

It was this little phrase, "next year", that triggered off Acky's brain to the explosive point of a new idea: "Next year! That's something to go on: you can set down and think about what you're going to do next spring, the same as you scheme to plant out the owd yard with vegetables and things." And he had many sittings on the rough seat in his garden, smoking his pipe and milling over the white blackbird's possibilities. Then one day he tapped his pipe on the seat and went indoors humming a tune—a rare thing for Acky. He spent most of the following Saturday at the *Plough*; and at last he met the man he was looking for: the retired colonel who spent so much of his time bird-watching.

This Colonel Quy was an unusual man for an ex-army officer. He was tall and as straight as a ramrod, a typical "regular", you'd say. But in fact he was none of your *What! What!* colonels. He was quiet-spoken, wore glasses and was a bit like a parson in his manner. But he knew what he wanted, and he got it. Acky, of course, had ferreted out all about him, after seeing him for the first time in the *Plough* a year or so before. He told Sarah about him shortly after he'd got to know him over a pint of beer:

"When I fust meet him I say to myself, 'You're a right rum 'un, bor.' But between you and me he's a rare nice feller. Chance times he get his mate, Judge Ponder, to stay with him up at Barnfield Hall; and they go out a-watching buds. I see 'em on the Common many a time afore I meet him at the *Plough*."

Nothing more was said about the colonel; but just after the following Christmas Acky met him in the pub, and he soon got him into a corner and told him:

"Come the spring, Colonel, I'll show you a bud you've niver seen in your life afore, as rare a bud as any you've seen in Suffolk."

The colonel was very interested; and he arranged that Acky, as soon as the white blackbird turned up to build its nest again, should get in touch with him; and he would then bring his friend the judge over to see it.

Now that this was fixed, Acky had to persuade Sarah to fall in with his scheme—he had already got it worked out—but he decided to leave that until the bird actually appeared. "There's no sense", he told himself, "in a-crossing of bridges until you come to 'em." But he did start building a wooden contraption, like a narrow shed, at the far end of the garden away from the spot where the birds had previously nested. And when

Sarah had asked him what he was doing he told her: "I'm kinda experimentin'. Maybe our hins will lay better in a place o' this particular shape."

Soon life began to stir again in the earth; the evenings to draw out and the buds and then the leaves to show themselves on hedge and bush; and the birds to bustle about their yearly job of setting up house again. But no white blackbird appeared; and another blackbird—an ordinary run-of-the-mill bird with nothing more distinctive than a will to get on with the job—turned up and set to work building a nest in the very same part of the garden as the white one had done. Acky chased it away, and did his best to discourage it from returning. But it still came back; and as there was no sign of the rare one Acky was beginning to get worried. The colonel had already called twice to inquire about the bird; and when Acky had to tell him that it had not yet arrived, he looked at him as though he were letting down the regiment.

After another week had passed and there was still no sign of the bird, and the interloper and his mate had settled down seriously to build, Acky became desperate and even began thinking of some wildcat scheme or other to catch the interloper and daub him with a bit of white in order to prevent his plan from foundering altogether. Fortunately, on a beautiful sunny morning the bird itself turned up, as white and as cocky as ever. Acky spotted him in the garden where he'd gone before breakfast to prepare a bed for his carrots; and there and then he saw the *white 'un* give the interloper a drumming and send him off without much ceremony.

"Now we can git on, gel," Acky said, rubbing his hands; "I'll send a card tonight, and the colonel and his mate will be up afore tomorrow's out; or if the judge ain't up at Barnfield, they'll be along the day after. Now this is the way o' things,

E   65

Sarah. The colonel and the judge will watch this bird from the sentry-box. There's a right fine view through the window: I find thet out last year." Acky chuckled. "It will be right and proper to have the colonel in the sentry-box, don't you think, gel?"

"The sentry-box!" Sarah said bristling up. "What do you mean?"

"You know right well what I mean: the House o' Commons down the garden; the villa where the honeysuckle grow—the lavatory!"

"Whatever next!" said Sarah, taking off her apron and throwing it over a chair. "Oh, no, they won't! I reckon you've overreached yourself this time. You can't have them in there!"

Acky had half-expected this opposition; and that was one of his reasons in leaving any mention of his tactics until the very last moment. He knew now that he would have to begin talking:

"Hold you a minute, gel. You fare not to understand this bird-watching business. Look, these people got to have a *hide* —that's what they call it—a place where they can hide up so the birds can't see them but they can see the birds."

"I don't care what they call it. They can't go in there. I'm whoolly surprised you should have thought of it. What . . . what if I . . . well, what if someone want to go. . . ."

"Now don't you worry about thet, Sarah," Acky said soothingly, "I fixed up the temporary place, for a summer-house like. We can go there."

"That chicken-place you said you were a-building! Oh, you rogue, Acky Flatt!" She could hardly speak from the indignation she felt; but as soon as she recovered she changed her line of attack:

"I'd be ashamed to ask these people—a colonel and a judge, you say—to spend most of a day in there. I don't know how you have the cheek to ask them!"

"Oh," said Acky. "I reckon they don't mind where they go when they're out campaigning. And the judge, I reckon that judge will be right lucky if he don't have to set on a more uncomfortable bench than what's in there. They'll have a right good view of the nest and the birds; and that's all they'll be consarned with. If you don't mind making a pot o' tea now and then, I shan't mind taking it down to them. We can put all that on the rent."

"The rent?"

"Whoi, of course, the rent they'll be paying on the sentry-box."

Sarah made no comment. She pursed her lips and took up her apron and tied it on again slowly. There was a hard light in her eye. Acky looked at her and shrugged his shoulders: "And now, I reckon, she's up to suthen!"

And Sarah was. When the two bird-watchers arrived on the following morning she welcomed them as though they were her guests which in a sense they were; and she made them as comfortable as she could under the very extraordinary circumstances. She made the tea and she herself took it down to them, making Acky run the touch-line; a hard thing for him to do because he couldn't even talk or argue with her for fear of frightening away the bird.

The colonel and the judge settled in very comfortably and they were both very enthusiastic about the view they had of the nest and the two birds—particularly the rare one which seemed to be coming and going the most. They wrote sheaves of notes, took two or three films, and were generally as pleased as if they had discovered gold. And while the birds were nesting and rearing their brood they came down and watched them from their hide at least on one day every week. Each time they came Sarah waited on them, gently manœuvring Acky into the background. When he protested she said firmly:

"The house is my concern, and I consider the 'Little House' is part of it—a proper part of the house."

On the last day of the bird-watching when Judge Ponder—a short man who just reached the colonel's shoulder—had to go back to London, Sarah invited them into the parlour and gave them a glass each of her elderberry wine. Then the colonel made a little speech thanking them both and handed Sarah an envelope—a little token of their regard for all she'd done for them. When they had gone Acky looked hard at Sarah counting the notes. She put them back in the envelope and stowed it carefully under the clock.

"That were a fine idea of yours, Akerman. I reckon I'll now be able to buy some new curtains with that. Good thick 'uns to keep us warm when that old wind blows from the east."

"Yeh," said Acky, who was still looking at the envelope under the clock. "I could think o' suthen that'd keep the cowd out better'n your curtains. But never mind, gel! You wait till next year. That owd bird will be back again; and if I don't work out a better sort o' carry-on than we've had this year, my name is not Akerman Flatt."

8.

Cure by Kindness

If anyone tackled Acky about his poaching he would tell him that, far from going against the law, he was a real public benefactor. "What sort of a corn-crop", he'd say, "would the farmers be a-getting if I wasn't helping to keep the birds down?"

But poaching was in Acky's blood and came as naturally to him as breathing. They say he was able to wring a pheasant's neck when he was in his cradle; and maybe this is no exaggeration. For Acky's father, after a night's work, would often hang his birds round the children's cot, covering them with blankets in case a caller should come at the wrong time and show an interest in the size of his wife's larder before the birds had been sent to their proper quarters—which were usually behind the back door of a certain fishmonger and poultry-dealer in Fordham.

Most of Acky's birds came from Fenhall Grange which was owned by the Vesey family. Now there was a feud between the Flatts and Veseys, going back for generations; and it was all on account of the poaching. But as far as Acky was concerned there was no enmity at all: there was only a little difference of opinion with the Veseys about sharing the pheasants and the partridges that strutted over their land. If they could have caught Acky at his poaching perhaps it would have developed into something warmer than a mere difference of opinion; but the fact was that Acky was very difficult to catch. He never went to the same place on two successive occasions, however good the poaching; and he was none of your fly-by-night, shoot-and-run poachers who would blaze away at a covey of pheasants roosting in the pine trees, grab a couple of them as they fell and then run hell for leather before the keepers came after him.

No, Acky had a bit of science; and he was much less spectacular, but much more efficient and much harder to come near to when he was out on one of his night jaunts. He'd take a small tin along with him in his pocket, and a bamboo cane about eight feet long—just as though he were going out fishing. And when he came up with a few pheasants roosting in a tree, he'd light the rags he'd stuffed into this tin, thrust the cane into a hole specially made in it, and then hold the other end of the cane under the nose of the drowsing pheasant. After a few seconds of Acky's smoke and smother down would plop the pheasant like a ripe apple off a bough; and Acky had only to wring its neck and conceal it in his deep pocket before working on the next one.

Another trick of his was to make little paper cones and smear the inside with treacle. He'd put a little corn inside them, and then place them in the field, scattering a few grains of corn around them. Then he'd crouch in the hedge to wait for what turned up. It wouldn't be long before the birds were out exploring, and they had soon thrust their heads into the sticky cones and were running about not knowing whether they were coming towards Acky or escaping from him.

Ted Finbow, the keeper, had no chance of catching him. Ted knew this; and although nothing was said, a kind of understanding developed between them, as plain as if the keeper had told him: "Now look you here, Acky: I know you're a-taking the birds; but I've not yet had the catching of you. And if you don't go making a rare business out of it, I won't be coming up after you too fast, you may depend."

This arrangement suited well, for Acky didn't make much of a business out of it (it was different from the old days when wages were so low he had to do something on the side); and out of consideration for Ted Finbow he took only a pheasant or two when he fancied one for his own table. But then old Mr. Vesey died; and his wife, instead of settling down to become a respectable widow, as she should have done, took it into her head to manage the estate herself. That was when the fun started. She stirred things up and looked into places where no light had been seen for generations. And Ted Finbow wasn't his own master any longer. The old girl chased him from backhouse to covey, and back again. She said there weren't half as many birds on the estate as there should have been. The land was being poached; and he'd better do some night-watching. It would do well for him to keep an eye on that man Flatt: she was sure he was taking scores of birds off the estate.

When Acky heard that the old girl had singled him out, he said:

"I'll sweep the place o' birds so the old harridan won't have a feather to put in her Sunday bonnet! 'That man Flatt!' she say! Well, I'll show the old will-jill, the owd man-woman, exactly what Akerman Flatt can do once he gets properly a-going."

But on thinking it over, his natural caution got the better of him. For he could see that if he stepped up his poaching, Ted Finbow would be the first to suffer for it. Old Mrs. Vesey would probably turn him off and get another keeper. Apart from the inconvenience this would cause Ted, it would be the last thing that Acky himself would want to happen.

Yet he could no more keep away from Fenhall Grange than

he could stop himself from fingering his ear-rings or scratching himself when a flea got under his shirt. One evening just before dusk, he was up there in the Park, skirting about in the scrub, when he saw Mrs. Vesey striding along, with Ted Finbow at her heels like a puppy dog she was just beginning to train. They were walking on the Long Meadow, and she was pointing and waving her arms about as though she were directing an army. He felt sorry for Ted Finbow. What a terrible thing it is when the woman measures herself for the trousers!

But what was she up to now? Acky went nearer to the field and saw that here and there were pairs of stakes, a couple of feet high, placed right across it. For the moment he was puzzled; and then he chuckled. His chuckle threatened to become a laugh so he drew back into the bushes in case they heard him. The old girl had got Ted to put small lengths of barbed wire all over the meadow to prevent anyone dragging it with nets. Nets! She was about as far off the mark as she could be: to think that the Park was being poached by a gang of chaps who used nets and walked up and down the field roping in the hares and rabbits exactly as if they were trawling herrings. She was about fifty years behind the times! Ted Finbow must have tried to tell her this. But Acky knew her sort. Once she'd got an idea in her head nothing but dynamite would shift it. He went home that night feeling much better disposed to old Mrs. Vesey. If she went about her gamekeeping like that there was nothing to fear from her. She was as harmless as the old *mawkin* they placed on the fields to scare the starlings.

Staying away from the Park, though, made Acky restless; and the duty he felt he owed Ted Finbow—to lay off the birds while the old girl was on the hunt—had made a bigger hole in his life than he could put up with. So one night, when he knew that Ted was over at Fordham visiting his sister who was ill, he decided to have a walk round the Park to see how things were faring. If he saw a chance of getting something, and he wasn't man enough to resist the temptation, he wouldn't think any the less of himself for that.

It was a moonlit night but he had no difficulty in getting about the Park without being seen. But as he entered the big covert he paused, thinking he had heard someone shouting. It was a cold night, and he buttoned his overcoat up to his neck and waited. Then hearing nothing more he went forward. He had not gone more than a hundred yards when he heard the cry again. Unmistakable this time, it came from the direction of the Long Meadow. His instinct told him to get out of the Park and keep away from trouble; but just as he was about to go back he realized that the voice he was hearing was a woman's. He hurried forward and stood in the bushes overlooking the Long Meadow, in exactly the same spot as he had done a few nights before.

What he saw now was even more surprising: a woman was lying on the ground near the centre of the field. As Acky went forward cautiously it looked as if she was struggling with something on the turf. Then another loud cry of, "Help! Help!" reminded him that he'd have to act. He went forward quickly and then he stopped: he seemed to know that voice. Whatever was the old girl doing out there? But she'd spotted him; and still lying as if pinned to the ground, she half turned and said with relief: "At last!" But Acky, as he came nearer, muttered to himself: "I fare to think this here is more like the beginning than the last." For it was old Mrs. Vesey! There was no mistaking her as he came up and she turned her head with difficulty towards him:

"Cut me loose!" she said quickly. "I'm all tangled in the barbed wire. It seems. . . ."

73

"That's all right, ma'am," Acky said promptly. "You lie right still. I'll have you free in no time."

He saw in a moment what had happened: she had taken a walk in the Park to keep an eye on her precious game, knowing that Ted Finbow was off duty, and she had gone full tilt into one of her barbed-wire traps; and now her skirt and her petticoats were all knotted up in a tangle it would take an hour properly to sort out. She could hardly move, for the harder she had struggled the more helpless she had become. Acky took out his knife and looked at the tangle.

"It's you, is it? I might have guessed! But hurry up. You'll have to cut me loose. You're a married man, aren't you? You're not scared of a petticoat!"

Acky went quickly to work and carefully cut the wire from her skirt and her underclothes. Then he helped her to her feet.

"Thank you," she said, in a different tone of voice, "I thought I'd be out here for the night. And that would have killed me. I'm afraid you'll have to come with me to the Grange, Akerman. My feet and legs are so numb with cold I can hardly put one in front of the other."

Before, therefore, he knew what was happening Acky was walking up the front drive with the lady hanging on his arm, just as though he'd called to pay his respects, had met her in the Park and was now escorting her home. As they approached the main entrance they saw the housekeeper who was just coming out to search for her mistress. She had a shock when she saw Akerman and looked at him as though she'd set the dogs on him. But Mrs. Vesey said:

"It's all right, Annie. Get me my woollen dressing-gown, and bring something hot. We'll have it in the library."

In a few minutes they were both sitting in front of a huge log fire. Acky was sipping at a glass of whisky, and Mrs. Vesey, soon getting up to pour herself her second glass, explaining firmly that she was a good deal colder than he was. Acky was bound to admire the old girl. A few minutes before she had hardly been able to speak from the cold; and yet now she was as alert and perky as one of her pheasants. She thanked Acky again for rescuing her; and she added in a very friendly way:

"You don't want to poach, Akerman. Poachin' is right out of fashion, you know. If ever you want a bird or a rabbit, or a hare for that matter, you only have to come here to the Grange. There's no need for you to go creeping about out there in the dark after them." Then with a delightful smile: "You and me are getting much too old for those kind of tricks!"

Now this made Acky get hot under the collar; but he couldn't explain his feelings to the old girl. He thanked her politely and left as soon as he could, making his way out of the grounds as fast as his legs could carry him. He told no one what had happened—not even Ted Finbow, who would have laughed until the cows came home just to hear it. And a change came over Acky after that. He gave up his poaching because there was a lot in what the old girl said, so he told himself, about getting too old for the business. But, naturally, he didn't call at the Grange as Mrs. Vesey had suggested. For what self-respecting poacher would go asking for game in that way? But that was not the end of it. A couple of weeks later Ted Finbow had orders to take a brace of pheasants along to Acky's cottage. And what self-respecting poacher could go out on the job after that?

"I never would have thought I'd come to it," Acky told Sarah that evening while they were making a meal of one of the pheasants. "I reckon this is the first time I've tasted a bird from the Grange that didn't come out at the backdoor. Some say it tastes sweeter when you've won the bird yourself. But

I'm right certain this bird tastes as sweet as any I've borrowed from the old gel. She's kinda killing us with kindness. Some 'un has been a-telling her you'll ketch more flies with a spoonful o' honey then you'll git with a gallon o' winegar. Enjoy yourself, Sarah. She's right! Whichever way you looks at it, I'm a-getting too old to go scrabbling about in the dark after pheasants."

9.

The Re-education of Mr. Carson

One of the jobs Acky did when he retired from the farm was to help old John Marjoram restore Fenhall post-mill. After Albert Pretyman, the miller, had died just at the end of the war, old John, the millwright, had taken over; and he kept the mill going for ten years until the new mills put it out of business.

John Marjoram's wife had died shortly after the mill stopped work; and Acky used to call in at his cottage just by the mill to have a chat and to walk round the garden and inspect the flowers and vegetables. During one of his calls Acky noticed how the mill had already begun to show signs of neglect: some of the weather-boards had slipped off the buck, and two of the steps up to the mill were missing; and the stocks, the arms of the mill, looked shaky.

"It fare to make you feel adrift", he told John, "to see the owd mill going down like that."

John shook his head and turned his back after giving the mill a glance.

"Yeh, Acky. It's like having some'un dying afore your eyes. But there it is! I suppose we all got to come to it; and they don't want the owd mill any more. Though it come hard to a fellow ha' known her all his life and sarved 'prentice to her well over fifty year agoo."

A few days after this Acky met Dr. Bulley on one of his

visits to the village; and when he stopped to have a word, Acky mentioned the state of the mill.

"You are not the only one who's concerned about it, Akerman," Dr. Bulley told him. "You get your Clerk—Joe Easy, isn't it?—to put the mill on the agenda for the next Parish Council meeting; and I'll see what I can do at Ipswich."

Dr. Bulley lost no time. He stirred up both the local M.P. and the chairman of a sub-committee of the County Council; and he got Joe Easy to write a letter to the *Mercury*. Within the year, word came through to County Hall that the Ministry of Works had decided to take over Fenhall post-mill and to restore it. The first news John Marjoram had of this was from two Ministry men who turned up at his cottage. The elder of the two, a tall grey-haired man, introduced his companion as "Mr. Carson, who is the architect in charge of the restoration". They both assumed that John would agree to do most of the actual repair-work with any help he could get in the neighbourhood. When he heard their plan John took off his cap and scratched his thick, grey hair:

"Yes," he said, trying to conceal his feelings, "I'll do it." And the tall man patted him on the shoulder and told him that Mr. Carson had arranged to stay at Fordham while the work was going on. Mr. Carson, a stocky man with a fair, well-trimmed beard, smiled in a friendly way and arranged to meet John at the mill on the following Monday morning.

As soon as the two men left his cottage, John went to call on Acky:

"They got a bit o' sense up there in Lunnon after all," was Acky's verdict on the news. "Some on 'em can see farther than their own back yards, seemingly. They mun know they couldn't let Fenhall mill sink into the ground like last year's leaves. When are you a-figuring to start, John?"

They met at the mill early on Monday morning; and they did not have long to wait for Mr. Carson. He arrived with a briefcase fat with plans, notes and pamphlets. Old John's face was shining with excitement. He was beginning a new chapter in the history of the mill. He had no drawings or notes of any kind; but he had a clear picture in his mind of the way he was going to tackle the restoring job. Acky, for the moment, stood in the background after John had introduced him to Mr. Carson. He saw exactly how the field was arranged, and he watched the two antagonists closely. Old John had spent the week-end and one or two almost sleepless nights carefully working out in his head how they were going to go about the job: he had a clear and detailed plan of how it was to be done. But so had Mr. Carson. After all, when you think about it, wasn't he the architect, and a Ministry architect at that?

"Best start at the stocks," said John, after the first skirmishings were over; "have a look at these first and then see to the mill itself."

"The post," Mr. Carson said firmly, taking out one of his carefully drawn plans. "That's the important thing: we'd better examine that first."

"I can tell you about thet, sir," John said confidently. "And you can see for yourself. The post will last for another hundred year without touching on it. Yeh, the post will do! Don't worry about that, Mr. Carson."

But most of the first day was spent in a preliminary inspection, and they managed to avoid a head-on clash. After that it was anvil and hammer, with old John as the tough, immovable anvil. Before the end of the week, Mr. Carson returned to London, leaving detailed written instructions, along with the plans, of how he wanted John to carry on while he was away.

"Telling me how to go on in Fenhall mill!" old John said to Acky. "Why, I could find my way over this place with my eyes shut and tell him what's wrong into the bargain. And I wouldn't want any plans or papers to help me put it right!"

"Tell you what, John," said Acky, nodding his head in sympathy; "you'n me better git on, plough our own stetch togither; and forget about all them draughts on the table there. Do the best we can. And I reckon it'll be as good as Mr. Carson is likely to git out o' the papers there."

Therefore they carried on working in their own way, and at their own speed, with John Marjoram pausing now and then to deliver himself of the gentle spleen that had for the time clouded his blood:

"Mr. Carson's all right you mun understand, Acky; only he's been a-spending too much time up thar in that Ministry a-reading o' books and things. He's not a *practical* man like you and me. He don't fare to see it the way we do. But that's it, when you come to it, it wouldn't do for us all to be alike. Would it? It take all sorts to make the world."

"Yeh," said Acky, "and by the look on it nowadays it take more'n a few to make the owd mill goo round—different to what it used to be, John. But where there's wit there's wealth. Both on us know the way to do it; we've got the *know* and that will get us hoom."

So John and Acky went on, slowly renovating and making repairs in the mill exactly as they would have done if they hadn't seen Mr. Carson in their lives. By the end of the week they were very pleased with the headway they were making. But when the architect returned from London and saw that his instructions and plans were still lying under the piece of flint on the table, the papers neatly folded and as clean as when he left them, he took a quick look round the mill and lost his temper. His face was white as he went off into a tirade about following his instructions and doing the job properly. But John Marjoram just looked at him calmly, and when he had finished he said:

"See here, Mr. Carson. No offence when we didn't look at your draughts. But this is how I see it. You can't goo a-putting this owd mill down on paper like this—as so many joins and joints, so many pegs and cogs and spars. It's jus' as though a young chap were to goo and make a draught o' the gel he were a-wanting to wed. If he's got anything in him at all, he see her and then he go arter her without beating about the bush. Now it's like this here with Acky and me, Mr. Carson. We can see what is to be done and we goes and we do it. When I first see this owd mill more years agoo than I'd like to recollect, I took a proper fancy to har; and I been a-tending har and a-shaping on har up for most o' the time ever since. But when you come along and show me a draught and say to me: 'That's the old mill. That's how she ought to be,' I can't take any account of it at all. That's not the mill I know, I mun tell you. Thet's some other mill that you got in your own hid!"

Mr. Carson's face showed his feelings. He couldn't trust himself to answer the old man, fearing to bring on a row; so he muttered something about having a look at the stocks, and escaped outside.

As he walked round the mill yard, not even glancing at the mill itself but lost in his problem, he quickly saw there was little he could do. These two men were the only ones in miles who could do the work; and he was entirely in their hands, especially as he had been given a date for the official opening of the mill to the public; and all the work would have to be completed by then. It went against the grain. But what else could he do? Better to let the two old chaw-porks have their head, and for him to keep a tolerant eye on them, than for him to have a row on his hands and the work held up entirely. He decided to keep away from the mill as much as he could, letting them do the work more or less in their own way, keeping a check only on the amount of timber they were using so that the job wouldn't exceed the budget he had been given. Therefore he turned up at the mill most mornings, had a quick look round and then spent most of the day sketching and measuring up a nearby moated manor-house that had been scheduled for preservation.

Left to themselves John Marjoram and Acky got into a steady rhythm and the work went ahead smoothly.

"The old gel is beginning to look herself again," John told Mr. Carson one morning. "We'll get her in right shape and trimmed up good tidily well afore the day when we are a-going to show her."

"Yes," agreed Mr. Carson, pleased in spite of himself with the way the mill was coming along; pleased, too, with his own diplomacy in *humouring* the old man, as he called it. "Yes, the mill is certainly looking better than it did. When we've given it another coat of paint, I think it'll be ready for the opening."

"Yeh," said Acky, who had by this time worked himself well into the "company", "but I reckon we'll have to dress the stones, Mr. Carson, to make a right proper job of it."

John Marjoram backed Acky up, but the muscle in Mr. Carson's face began to twitch again. "There's no need to dress the stones," he said precisely. "We're not going to grind any corn. And our instructions are quite clear, if you'd take the trouble to read them: *do not move the stones unless this is absolutely necessary*. We'll leave the stones as they are!"

The Re-education of Mr. Carson

Without waiting for a reply Mr. Carson turned quickly and walked out to his car. As he made for the manor-house he was glad that the mill job was coming on so well; glad, too, that he had at last put his foot down and shown the two old hammer-swingers who exactly was the boss.

But to John Marjoram and Acky the job was far from being nearly finished. To restore a mill without putting the stones themselves into proper order was like curing a sick man, giving him back his appetite and then leaving him without any teeth.

"He's not going to grind any corn he say," old John grumbled as they watched the architect's car disappearing. "You know, Acky, he's as rigid as that owd post in the centre of the mill!"

"Wait a while, John," said Acky; "that ain't right. If that owd post were half as stiff as he is, it would have split itself into smithereens years agone by. Did you see how he got wild the other day? I reckon he don't do himself no good a-going on that way. He were so wild and het up you could ha' boiled a kittle on the top of his head. He won't make owd bones that way!"

John Marjoram and Acky quietly put Mr. Carson in his place; and as a result of their little discussion they decided not only to dress the millstones but actually to grind a sack or two of corn. Only in this way, so John Marjoram maintained, could a master craftsman properly round off his job to his own satisfaction. And he considered he wouldn't be doing wrong even if Mr. Carson didn't agree with him. So when the architect left on the following day for London, John and Acky set to work on the stones: they took off the runner- or top-stone—and proceeded to deepen the *furrows* and score the *land*, the flat part of the stones that actually ground the corn. As it happened both the runner- and the bed-stones were in bad shape, and the job took much longer than old John had estimated. Two days later Mr. Carson walked in while they were still at it. This time he lost his temper completely and stormed about the mill like a tyrant. Old John regarded him for a while and then said evenly:

"All right, sir. Have it your own way. But howd hard a minute while I tell you suthen about this stoon. You see here it's got four furrow to ivery section. Us country chaps hev a special name for each one. The tiddy one is the *butterfly*, the back'us boy, as you might say. This here is the *'prentice*; the next is the *journeyman*, and the biggest o' the lot is the *maaster* furrow —the Minister o' Works, if you like. But the Minister, he say he can't git away from his office, so he send you—all right and proper! But look at me! I bin a journeyman for most o' ma life, and I now got a mind to be Maaster. No, wait a minute, don't you git windy! I'm a fair man, and I'll tell you what I'll do. Let me be Maaster for the next couple o' days till the owd mill's open; and then you can be Maaster for the rest o' your natural life."

Mr. Carson didn't even trouble to answer. He snorted and walked out of the mill in a rage. But he gave his answer unequivocally on the following day. As soon as the stone was back in position he locked the mill; pocketed the key; and told John and Acky quite casually that he hoped he'd see them at the opening ceremony.

The next morning the two came to work as usual; and stood on the triangular green in front of the locked mill. There was a stiff sou'westerly breeze blowing; and they looked at the mill, its stocks all white and resplendent—and perfectly idle.

"It's a shame to have them like thet!" Acky said.

"We can't have them like that, Acky bor. We'll hev to do suthen!"

"What if I goo down to ma place and git my owd fold-pritch? I'd only hev to show it to thet lock—suthen would hev to give. But wait a minute, I forgit myself. I brought a few keys along that might suit our business."

As Acky took the keys out of his pocket and started to try them in the lock, John Marjoram said:

"Yeh, you see to it, Acky. We're going inside! I'll go along and git that comb o' wheat that's been a-waiting for this day. It's down there in ma owd shed."

It was a fine day for the opening ceremony and a big crowd of local people and Dr. Bulley and a few notables from Ipswich attended. The ceremony itself went off smoothly and Mr. Carson was very pleased with himself. He shook hands and chatted cordially with his two helpers. Then John Marjoram took him gently by the arm and led him a little distance from the crowd to a small table on the green:

"Acky and me would like to give you a present, Mr. Carson," and he then handed him two small loaves of honey-coloured bread, neatly wrapped in a white linen cloth.

"Yeh, ma Sarah baked 'em only this morning. So they're right fresh from the brick-oven."

"One for yourself, Mr. Carson," old John said, still holding him by the arm as though he would walk away before he had finished what he had to say, "one for you and one for the Minister o' Works. Do you tell him where it come from; and when he taste that he can be right certain his mill at Fenhall is in proper working order. And he can be sure he's not wasted good public money for nothing but a peep-show."

10

The Auction Sale

Few people in Fenhall ever mentioned the famous auction sale at Thatch Farm to Akerman Flatt; for although it happened nearly fifty years before he still didn't want to talk about it. And if anyone approached Sarah, hinting at Acky's part in it, she would turn off the questioner by telling her: "Oh, that was in his young days when he had even more bone in his head than he's now got."

It happened just after Acky and Sarah got married. Acky was then horseman to Edgar Lartman who at that time farmed at the Thatch, the farm away out on the outskirts of the parish. Those were the days of "all horses", before a tractor had been seen in Fenhall. It was the environment in which Acky had been formed; and even when he was a young fellow there was little you could tell him about farm-horses. They were in his blood: his father and his grandfather had been horsemen on the farms round Fenhall; and, as he used to say, it was only because his family memory was a short one that stopped him going back much further than that, when he was sure you wouldn't find a Flatt without his having something to do with horses. Acky knew his business and because he was also a good hand with the plough he became "head horseman" or foreman at the Thatch. Edgar Lartman, the farmer, in choosing Acky had recognized a good craftsman; but there was also another reason for his choice: in passing over the older horsemen on his farm he wanted to get his own back for the trouble they had caused him. But the whole bottom of the matter was that this Edgar Lartman was a strange employer; and he had got the men's back up so high that they began to *look* as though they were carrying their load of grudges round with them, as indeed they were. You could pick out just two of these as a sample of the rest.

It was the time when all the cottages were tied as close to the farm as the hames to a horse's collar. Lartman had exchanged some words with one of his workmen and he had given him the sack. But the man, Jack Inkpen, had turned stubborn and wouldn't move out of his cottage. He just sat there with his wife and two children and kept all unlikely looking people away: he even threatened to shoot "owd Narrerback" with a 12-bore. (Narrowback was the men's name for Lartman: he wasn't very tall but he was as broad as a barn-door, and he had little eyes that seemed to lose themselves in his head.) This went on for a few days; and then one morning Tom, the third horseman who came to work past the Inkpen cottage, went over to Acky as he was baiting his team of horses. It was a grim morning in November, the sky emptying rain: "You know what owd Narrerback ha' done?" he told Acky. Acky paused as he placed a sieveful of bait into the horse's manger, and looked round at Tom Preston. "He's been and taken the tiles off Inky's roof."

"The what?"

"He goo down there with a ladder last night—I now see it *outside* the cart-shod not inside as it allus is—and he take the pan-tiles off the top o' the roof. I reckon Inky and his family are some damp already. The weather's been a-pouring through thet hole for a couple of hours. It fare to be like a shower-bath in there, I reckon."

Acky shrugged his shoulders. He'd just got married; and

he'd already set a steady course of his own: to get a bit of money together as soon as he could and be his own master by renting a few acres.

"Best to say nawthen, Tom. It ain't our quarrel."

"But it may well be, Acky! I reckon it could be one of us next."

"Best to git started, Tom. Leave it to those it consarns. Git your hosses baited, and you can take Boxer down to the forge to get that loose shoe fitted. It's too wet to turn out. You can get down thar 'arly and get first shoeing."

The other occasion was the harvest that followed this incident. Instead of letting Acky brew the harvest-beer, as was his right, Edgar Lartman decided to have it done himself. On the previous harvest he had complained to Acky that too much malt was going into the men's beer: it could be made much cheaper than that. As it turned out, the harvest when Lartman brewed the beer was outstanding: the yield of wheat was excellent, the barley was good enough even for the brewers; and there was no rain at all during the time they had to win it. But the beer was the worst that had ever been brewed on the farm; *Narrerback's beer* was never forgotten and became symbol for rock-bottom, the lowest quality of all. Rot-gut, Good Water Spoiled, Barrel-swillings, and Whip-belly, were some of the more polite names the men gave to it, but old Tom Preston described it more coolly:

"If it had been any wuss, we couldn't ha' drunk it: if it had been any better we shouldn't ha' had it!"

Therefore with a few ready instances of Lartman's *narrowness* always at the front of their minds, and a few judgements like, "He's a right fornicator: he'll tell you one thing to ya face and another ahind ya back!" and "He's so close he wouldn't give the fluff out of his navel away!" to stiffen up their attitude,

Lartman got so wrong with his men that things were quickly coming to a crisis. Then one evening when all the farmhands had gone home and Acky was on his own, having stayed behind to doctor a horse that had strained a shoulder, Lartman came into the stable:

"You better look for a job, Flatt," he said without preamble.

"You mean you're giving me the sack?" Acky asked, keeping as cool as he could.

"No! You know I wouldn't do that. You're the only good 'un in a bad bunch."

Acky wiped the oil from his hands on a piece of old sacking that hung over the partition between two stalls: "I'll have to be some careful", he told himself, "when Narrerback starts handing out compliments."

"No," the farmer went on, "I'm selling up. I thought to wait until next Michaelmas; but I've now decided to go at Lady's Day. I shan't tell the others till it's finally settled, so do you keep it close."

Then he walked out of the stable in his usual abrupt way, leaving Acky to think out a new situation and sort out the details as best he could. Acky reckoned he himself wouldn't have to worry about a job. If Lartman was clearing out, someone else would take over the farm immediately; and the new tenant would have enough sense not to sack the head horseman —at least not straight away. He was the one man who could put him right about the state of the land, and about a hundred other things he would need to know about the farm. But it would be a bit hard on the others: and he was pretty certain that some of them would be out of work until *haysel*, the hay-harvest in late May or early June; for Lady Day wasn't a good time to change jobs.

But by the time Acky got home that night he had put Lartman's visit to the stable out of his mind. He decided not to tell

Sarah anything about it. She was about to have their first child, and worrying over nothing wouldn't do her any good. But just as he was winding his watch before getting into bed that night he wondered: "Why did Lartman tell me about this here? There was no call for him to tell me so early. He's not the one for telling anyone more'n he has to. But it's best to sleep on that one"; and he placed the watch on the chair beside his bed and forgot about Lartman.

He had to wait three months before he got some light on the purpose of Lartman's visit to the stable. It was a fine day in February and Acky was out with a team of horses pulling down some land he had ploughed in the autumn. Lartman waited until Acky got to the headlands and rested his horses; then he came over.

"The frosts have broken it up right well," Lartman said, as he dug his heel into the crumbling soil.

"Yeh, but a few more wouldn't do it any harm"; Acky tied the cords to the plough-handle.

"I want to tell you about the auction. I got Groves from Fordham to do it. The bills will be out next week. Live and dead stock as well as the house stuff."

"You putting it all up then?"

"Yeh, I reckon to have a good sale—a wet one!"

"You mean you're going to supply the beer?"

"Yeh, you hit it! And I want you to brew it."

Acky looked at him: Just like that! as old Tom had told him in the stable the other day, 'He's full brother—or at least a half 'un—to the Owd Nick himself, with a face as hard and as bold as a brass monkey's.' But Acky grinned as he told Lartman out loud:

"But I kinda reckon you are the brewing expert."

Lartman's eyes showed his annoyance, but he answered smoothly enough:

"No, I'll have my hands too full with other matters for the next few weeks. I want you to do it. Make it strong. Tell me how much malt, hops, sugar and so on you'll need." And when he saw that Acky was making no move towards assent, he added: "I'll make it right for you."

"How right, Maaster?"

"Well, I tell you what I'll do for you. If the sale goes well, I'll give you the price of a couple of hogs. That will give you a start."

"But there mun be no *ifs* about it: you give me two hogs else it's no deal."

"Right! I'll do that. I want you to brew the beer next week, so it gets a little time to mature. I'll get the girls to give the brewing tackle a good cleaning, so it will all be ready for you."

Lartman went off and Acky turned his horses back towards the new stetch: "It's as plain now as the end of a barn. I can see owd Narrerback's drift as clear as a picture. I knew he were up to suthen; and I reckon I want my head read for not suspecting on it before."

During the past couple of years Thatch Farm, chiefly because of Lartman's high-handedness towards his men, had run down badly. The horses were overworked—in spite of Acky's protests; and, indeed, were it not for his skill they would have showed it much more than they did. The cattle were an indifferent lot; the milking herd should have been culled and strengthened with young blood at least three years before. Little of the deadstock was fit to be seen off the farm: the tumbrils and wagons had been neglected and hadn't seen a paint-pot since they were made, many years before. The ploughs, the harrows, the cultivators, the horse-hoes were nearly all in various stages of disrepair. If the men spent the next month in patching them up and the master a hundred pounds or so on the materials, they would hardly be fit for a worthwhile sale by

the 26th March or by any other day later in the year. But Acky
was correct in his suspicions. Most of the stock couldn't be
made right, but they could be made to *appear* to be right. The
way to do that was to have a wet auction: to give all the pros-
pective buyers a new kind of sight—an optimistic, early spring
abandon; fill them up with strong beer and let the beer do the
bidding.

The Thatch was a much happier place as the day of the
auction approached. Lartman was going; and although none of
the men on the farm—except perhaps Acky—could be sure of
being taken on by the new owner few of them were very
worried. It was a case of the Devil unknown being a much better
prospect than the Devil they already knew; no employer, they
believed, could be worse than Narrowback. So Acky brewed
the beer and smuggled out a pailful of the "sweet wort" to the
stables for the men to taste. For he knew that as soon as it was
in the two fifty-gallon casks it would be "key-beer" immediately. Lartman would keep it locked up as tight as his gold
sovereigns; and not even Acky would get access to it without
letting him know. But the men now worked readily with the
auctioneer's staff as well as doing their routine jobs about the
farm; and they laid out the handtools, the implements and
tackle not in use, on the field where the auction was to be held:
they cleaned up the stables, the net'us, the barns, and out-
houses without a murmur; and they finished up polishing and
oiling the harness just to show they had no quarrel with Acky.
But on Lartman's order they had to shift the harness out of the
harness-room; and he got two beer-stools and had the two
hogsheads of beer lifted on to them. The harness-room was a
strategic spot, right beside the entrance to the field where the
auction was to take place.

On the morning of the sale Lartman was about the farm as
early as Acky and the other baiters. A couple of hours later he

surprised them all by inviting them along to the harness-room to draw themselves mugs of beer. He looked a new man: he wore a dark suit and a clean shirt with a sober tie; and his eyes shone with something that was as near to good humour as the men had ever seen in him. But they sidled in to sample the beer as warily as if the harness-room had been booby-trapped. Acky's beer was the best he had made, and the extra malt and hops made it doubly worth drinking. There were grunts of approval: this was the best farm-beer they had tasted for years. They were not invited to fill their mugs a second time, though; and as they were going out Lartman called Acky to one side and told him:

"Put Tom Preston in charge o' the beer; and you come to the house for the key—about 9.30. They'll be starting to roll up by then. I think we can trust old Tom not to make a sot of himself."

Lartman locked the door and went back to the house; and as Acky walked to the stables he noticed the bill that was stuck on the cart-shed where the auctioneer's clerk had his table. He saw something he had previously missed: *Refreshments Provided* was printed in clear lettering at the bottom of the bill.

Later, after Acky had got the key of the harness-room and opened it up, he said to Tom Preston:

"We're going to have a mort o' customers, Tom; and it look as if you're going to be busy."

"Yeh," said Tom, sniffing round. "I reckon so, now the beer is some bit stronger than when we tasted it!"

"What do you mean?"

"Can't you smell it, bor? He's been a-lacing thet, Acky, you ma' depend."

Acky laughed: "You're right, Tom! I should ha' known it," he said, as he drew a drop of the beer and tasted it. "There's sense in everything Narrerback does even if it ain't the right sense. I filled those hogsheads right full to the very top; and he had to get rid o' some o' the beer. That's why he let us sup a drop. But where's he put the empties?"

"You won't have to look far for those, bor. See over there; they're in the brush-cupboard, I doubt."

He was right: they found a cardboard box underneath the cleaning rags and brushes; in it were half a dozen empty gin and whisky bottles.

"He's been a-speculating and I reckon he'll get his returns. You want to watch out how much o' this stuff you now sup, Tom!"

"Don't you fret about me, Acky. It's the ones who don't know what he's got in this beer you'll have to worry about."

It was not clear whether or not Lartman had somehow arranged to delay the auction; but, whatever happened, the sale was late in starting; and the man with the bell had to ring it vigorously outside the harness-room before the company moved out on to the field. It must have been one of the most difficult sales that Groves the auctioneer had handled. The bidding started briskly with the sale of a few old stack-tilts; the second lot was a number of handtools: scythes, a bagging iron, a reap-hook and one or two scythe-rubs. A couple of small farmers bid against one another and the lot went at a fair price. There had been an undercurrent of banter to the auctioneer's selling, right from the start; but it did not break out until the third lot: a collection of ditching tools. Groves offered the lot at £1, but no one bid. Then a farmer called out loudly to a huge man who stood a few yards away, his thumbs in his waistcoat pockets and a thick walking-stick hanging from his right hand:

"C'mon, Josh! Give him a start. These here are just what you want to keep your weight down."

There was a laugh and Josh good-humouredly called out:

"Ten bob!" and he was immediately answered by the other farmer. In a minute or two, four more had joined in the bidding;
and the tools were knocked down to the big farmer for £6.

"What's he going to do with those?" a farmer asked Acky.
"He must have two sets o' ditching tools on his farm already!"

The sale went on in this vein right through until mid-after-
noon with Lartman walking about as pleased as a hog in a
field of roots. About three o'clock he visited the harness-room
to ask Tom Preston how the beer was lasting. The old man
nodded towards two farmers who, with mugs in their hand,
were leaning towards each other like two china dogs on the
mantelshelf, talking with slow and deliberate emphasis.

"I reckon it'll outlast them two," Tom said. "They ain't been
near the field for an hour; and there are a few more like 'em."

Lartman nodded and returned to the field. There was still a
fair crowd following the auctioneer along the rows of implements and machines; and the bidding got even more wild as he
reached the last row. And when a rather battered corn-drill
that normally would have fetched about £15 was knocked
down for £60 even the auctioneer felt it was time to call a halt.
It wasn't very clear to anyone how the last couple of lots—a
few pig-troughs and an old tumbril—were disposed of.

Acky walked over to the harness-room to see Tom Preston.
"There'll be hell to pay for this, Acky, when they sober up.
The beer's all gone, but I reckon it's done its work."

"Thet it has! And Lartman will be lucky if he gets away with
it."

Just then the auctioneer's clerk, who had been sitting at a
table in the cart-shed, called out to a farmer who was on his
way out: "Your bill, Mr. Wilson." And as the auctioneer came
in from the field his face showed that he wasn't very pleased.

He was even less pleased, when at the very end when most of the crowd had left the farm, the clerk had to go looking round for four of the bidders who were sleeping off Acky's beer in various places in the farm buildings. He found one in the chaff-room adjoining the stable, one in the stables itself, and two others sprawling on a heap of straw in the Dutch barn. The clerk did not succeed in arousing them and had to fold up the bills and place them in their jacket pockets. Lartman was nowhere to be seen; and Acky found out that he had left a good hour before the sale had ended.

The people who spent the night on the farm woke up next morning angry men. One of them came through the stable as Acky was grooming a pair of horses that were going away later in the morning: "Where's Lartman?" he shouted; and seeing Acky called out: "Here's the fellow who did the dirty work for him! But Lartman will get nothing out of me!" The three other men, following closely behind him, took him out of the stable; and Acky, curry-comb in hand, watched them stumbling across the yard.

"Just as I thought," Acky said to Tom Preston who had come to the door to watch them, "they'll put all thet at my door. I was a right fule to have anything to do with it. But where is Lartman?"

"He's gone, I reckon, Acky. He didn't sleep at the farm last night; else my missus, she say, she would have seen the light."

"So ma' hogs ha' gone too, most likely," Acky said wryly.

"What you say, Acky?"

"O nawthen, Tom, nawthen. I reckon it's the last we'll see o' Narrerback. I doubt they've squeezed all the beer out of those hogsheads. I could do with a sup o' suthen this morning."

"You're right, Acky; there's not enough left in 'em to drown a fly. We mun give Narrerback best and call it a day!"

The Lartman affair bit deep into Acky. Although most people knew that Lartman was the villain, Acky felt that he had been linked with him. And though time is supposed to cure all, it did not leave his own self-respect unscarred. For years afterwards he mentioned the wet auction to no one. Then one evening while he and Sarah were talking about the Thatch, Sarah happened to bring in Lartman's name. Acky became silent, and for a few minutes fingered one of his ear-rings as he looked into the fire.

"I reckon the only real lessons you larn," he said at last, "is when you get hurt."

"You're brooding about thet Lartman."

"Yeh, how did you know?"

"He got right into your blood, didn't he? You want to talk about him chance times—purge yourself of him."

"Maybe you're right. You got to pay for your mistakes. I should have known that when I had to do with Lartman. But a fellow can't easily forget when a man's tricked you and dirtied you with some of his own pitch. But what burned me up most was afterwards when he goo down there to Felixstowe a-faring as if."

"A-faring as if!"

"Yeh, a-lording it: a-faring as if he's a gentleman!"

Sarah laughed.

"You needn't ha' fretted about that. No one would have mistaken Lartman for a gentleman!"

"You got his measure, gel. Nobody would. One o' ma hogs were more of a gentleman than him. Leastways they'd grunt when you give 'em suthen."

"Purge yourself of him bo'. Besides, Lartman must have been gone now for nigh on twenty year. You can't live along o' the dead, Acky Flatt—whether they be angels or just rum folk like Lartman."

11

Acky and Justice

One fine summer evening Acky said to Sarah: "I'll take you on thet trip to Ipsidge I promised you—if you're in a mind to come." Sarah, however, was undecided, and Acky pressed her:

"You want to git out more, gel. When was it you were last abroad? You're allus a-setting indoors: I reckon if you were an owd hin you'd ha' brought off three lots o' chicks since Christmas. You don't want to worry about the weather. It won't change. The gnats are a-weaving, and the swallows climbing up high; and look! the sky is as red as a soldier's coat. We can cycle over to Fordham and catch a bus from there. We can then come back what time we like."

Sarah was at last persuaded to fall in with Acky's plan; and early next morning they were standing on the pavement by the bus-stop in the market square at Fordham, after cycling the few miles from Fenhall and storing their bikes in Fred Partridge's house near by. Sarah was in a good humour and her best hat; and Acky had his horseman's suit on and a silk square or muffler tied round his neck with an expert knot at the side. His ear-rings caught the sun, and his face shone with good humour as he sniffed the fresh morning, and watched the small happenings of the street: the passers-by, the shopkeepers arranging some of their stock outside on the pavement, and the postman collecting the letters from a pillar-box. Then he chuckled and continued chuckling noisily until Sarah said sharply:

"What's got into you, bor? You'll have the whole street coming over to see what's up, if you don't give over."

"It's the white lady up there," Acky said, nodding towards the Butter Cross, the circular wooden structure that stood in the centre of what was once the town market. On its top was a splendid figure of Justice, with scales in one hand and a sword in the other.

"She allus was up there," said Sarah. "What's funny about her? I think she's very lovely."

"Ah, you're right, gel. You're right. She's some fine. But you're wrong about one thing. She ain't allus been there. She were missing for some long while. That's the reason I were a-chuckling. She remind me of Bertie Russett."

The bus came along just then; and after they had settled in their seats Sarah asked: "But what has Bertie Russett to do with the statue of Justice on top o' Fordham Butter Cross?"

"All in God's good time, like the parson say. You want to take a hint or two from Job. But the marrow o' the matter is I take Bertie Russett out with me one night to see what we could git. There was a particular covey over there at Fordham that I used to visit with Fred Partridge. But Fred had been called up. This were the first year of the war, rightly the second; it were in June 1940 or early July. I forget the exact date. But I recollect the night as though it were yesterday—What were we a-doing on yesterday?—No, clearer than yesterday! I could ha' gone out that night alone, but I got a particular cause to have some'un with me that night—not because of the keepers. They weren't looking for poachers then: like everybody else they were a-sarching for Garmans. It were a couple o' weeks after Dunkirk. And they reckon the Garmans were a-going to arrive from all sides: from the air, along the roads, up the rivers

from the coast, from under the ground a'most. The Home
Guard, Home Defence or whatever they used to call theirselves
were out in their droves night and day, all with their fingers
on the triggers o' their breech-loaders, their 303s, their 4.10s,
their 12-bores—anything they got under their stairs. Pikes out
o' the museum some on 'em had! Now I could manage the
birds and the keepers; but I didn't want to be mistook for a
Garman and have my backside peppered by a 12-bore, or ma'
skull stove in with a pike by some Home Defence billy who
were a-rearing to do his duty. So I take Bertie Russett along
with me to keep us both out o' trouble.

"Bertie were some keen. He were like a boy a-going on a
Sunday school treat as we set out that night. He wanted to try
out his owd man's gun, the kind you take down and hide in
your pocket; but I say to him: 'There are a rare lot too many
guns about tonight, Bertie. We'll leave that at hoom, and we'll
just use our wits; atween us, I doubt, we got enough o' them to
win ourselves our breakfast. And leave that pipe o' yourn in
the drawer, Bertie. We'll keep a total blackout, like they say.'
You recollect at that time o' day, you could get a good price
for a rabbit. Folk weren't too particular; anything would do if
you could put it into the pot.

"It were some quiet as we made our way out toward Fordham. There were no raids, no anti-aircraft guns a-barking and
a-shattering the night—that come later in the year. But the
searchlights were a-flitting across the sky like the spokes of a
big wheel; and chance times two would stay right still and
make a kinda big pyramid o' light—a tent big enough to put
two counties in.

"These Guards were everywhere: at the bridges, the cross-
roads, the electric pylons, the charch—anywhere they think the
Garmans might take a fancy to. Me and Bertie know we had to
go some careful. But we got round them half-tidy; and we got

over to this covey, about half past eleven it were. We'd already
got a bagful o' rabbits. For you ma' depend, once you got away
from the road and the houses you could go on as you like. They
were a-letting the game to look arter itself: there was bigger
game afoot; everybody were after Garmans! So Bertie and me
had it all to ourselves; and we were doing right well and really
couldn't carry much more, and were thinking of making our
tracks towards hoom. But then of a sudden Bertie put up his
hand, warning like, dropped his bag and hared off out in front
somewhere, moving as silent as Sunday. And I'd been out with
Bertie afore, and I knew his gait, so I stay right still where I
were. He come back in half a minute breathing hard:

" 'It's the Garmans, Acky,' he say. 'Four on 'em. I see 'em
as plain as you!'

" 'Where?' I say.

"It weren't pitch dark, and once you'd got used to it you
could see middling tidy.

" 'Just to the other side o' that hedge. They come across that
meadow. Four on 'em; and they carried suthen with 'em. They
stop right there', he whisper, 'near that spinney in the corner
o' the meadow.'

" 'C'mon,' I say to Bertie, 'we'll have a peek at 'em. But
don't say nawthen. Keep dumb till I give you the down.'

"So we move forward quickly and got to the hedge, another
twenty yards and I see 'em! Bertie was right: there were four
on 'em with a big black thing on the ground beside 'em. And
now they were a-digging as though they were on piece-work.
Me and Bertie laid under that hedge a-watching on 'em. There
they were a-digging down and down, taking turn—two and
two about—till they were nigh out o' sight. Then one on 'em
say, quiet-like: 'Thet will do, lads!' and the two who were in the
hole threw up their shovels and they come out. Then they
lowered this big, black thing into the hole and started a-filling

in the hole like they were a-covering up murder. Afore they finish I put my hand on Bertie's shoulder and give him the *go-back*; and we make for the place where we left our bags. Bertie picked up his and was away in front; and after we been walking for some while he stop and he say: 'Them weren't Garmans, Acky!' He were a bit annoyed as though someone had tricked him. 'Him that spoke, I know 'un right well.' So I stopped and I say:

" 'You're right, Bertie. They ain't Garmans; not one on 'em have ever been across the water. But see here, Bertie: you and me ain't seen nawthen tonight! Nawthen! Do you git the drift o' that, Bertie?'

"His head were down as though he were a-weighing this up some hard; and then he look up sly-like:

" 'No, Acky,' he say, grinning. 'We ain't seen a thing.' "

Acky stopped and looked out of the window of the bus and pointed to a field of corn they were passing. "He got a rare field o' barley there, Sarah. It'll make Burton barley, I doubt."

Sarah looked at him with annoyance: "But what happened? What was it they were a-burying? Or is it you're going to keep the second part o' your serial till the next time we go to Ipsidge?"

Acky chuckled:

"That's a rare idea, gel. That would stop your puttering; jus' tell you a serial-story and not give you a chance! I mun think about that right hard. But I thought you could put the ends of the story togither now that I started you off; without me having to spell out every word of it for you."

"Get on with it," said Sarah.

"Well, I didn't see Bertie for a few days after that jaunt; and on the Saturday I take my owd bike to Fordham to get some parmit or other (it were all parmits at that time o' day: parmits for meat, parmit for butter, parmit for this and parmit for that, parmit for pigs, a parmit to breathe a'most!). And I meet Bertie a-cycling along with his head down. He look a bit down-in-the-mouth, too; and when I say, 'Hi, Bertie!' he say:

" 'I got my calling-up papers, Acky.'

"You see, he come off the land and got himself a job up at the aerodrome, because there was more money in it. And that were it! With a month they nab him and he were in the army afore he knew one side o' the runway from the other. So when I see how it was with Bertie I took him to Fordham *Lion* to cheer him up; and after a pint or two he were holding his head much higher. Then we come out and stand on the pavement, right there where we were now a-waiting for this bus. And two o' the Fordham folk come along, two women; and one on 'em look up and say:

" 'My goodness! She's gawn!'

" 'What?'

" 'She's gawn. Her with the scales and the sword: Justice! Whativer's happened to her?'

"And afore the other could open her mouth, owd Bertie he turn to har and he say:

" 'She's been called up, ma'am. Most o' the J's ha' gone some weeks since. But seemingly they're not so quick a-gitting them into the A.T.S. or the W.A.A.F.; or maybe they've made a sailor of her and put her in the W.R.E.N.S.'

"And Bertie look at me some cunning. He knew. He knew! He spotted it afore I did. And they say that Bertie were only fifteen ounces!"

"You mean", asked Sarah, "this Bertie had guessed what you saw that night when you were out poaching?"

" 'Course he did! Four on 'em; and I knew every man jack of 'em. All from Fordham. They put her away for fear of the Garmans. A rare night's work: a-burying Justice! And it didn't need a passon to git a moral out o' thet. In the war they say she is one o' the first to git the warm end o' the stick; and there she were right out o' sight, with her mouthful o' dirt; she couldn't speak up or nawthen—buried for the duration."

Sarah snorted: "You should ha' been a passon yourself! But they must ha' got her back! We now see her. It's the same one as before the war, ain't it?"

"Yeh," said Acky, with one of his knowing high-pitched laughs. "They got her back safe, and she were none the worse; but it were a rare lot o' trouble."

"Well, you better tell me the rest of the story. We got four or five miles yet to reach Ipsidge."

"Right, gel," Acky said, after a mischievous pause of a minute or two, just to keep Sarah on the hook. "Well, it were like this. After that day at Fordham I clean forgot about Justice. Bertie Russett went to the war; and all thet business went clean out o' ma hid. And you mun know there were plenty o' things to fill it up: the horses, the pigs, and the Home Guard which they got me into myself later on; and then there were the children, and all manner o' what-not: parmits, licence-papers! And as you well recollect it went on for years after the war finished. But four or five year after the war is over owd Fred come over here from Fordham—suthen about his pigs, most likely—and I say to him, not meaning much, jus' giving him the sele o' the day like:

" 'How are things in Fordham, Fred?'

"And he laugh, and he say: 'Oh, they're in a rare muddle over there. They're all a-calling one another names; and the Town Reeve he's nearly out o' his mind. They reckon they're going to make a case out of it!'

" 'Glass or boards?' I say. But owd Fred, without paying any regard, say:

" 'Naw! They say they're a-going to pull the Council!'

" 'Pull the Council!'

" 'Yeh, they threaten to have the whole bunch of 'em up in court. They reckon that some'un has nobbled Justice—that statue that used to be on the Butter Cross. Some say they hide har at the start o' the war because of the Garmans. Some say, Yeh! That's right. But they can't find her! And most on 'em say—or *think*, leastways, even if they don't say—that some'un up and sold her. She were made o' lead, you recollect; and you ma' know how much lead is a-fetching. She were a rare thing, Acky. I doubt you remember har. She were a right strappin' wench. She were the fust thing I miss in Fordham when I come out o' the army.'

" 'I recollect har right well,' I say. 'But what does the Town Reeve say in the matter?'

" 'He say he knows nawthen about it. And he's loike to be right.'

" 'O' course he's right. This 'un sartinly knows nawthen. He weren't in Fordham at that time o' day. John Bailey were the Reeve; and he got himself killed with that flying-bomb. He were the one that buried her.'

" 'Buried her!' Owd Fred looks at me as though he were a-seeing me for the first time. 'What you know about this here, Acky?'

" 'I reckon I better come over to Fordham and sort things out,' I say, 'afore you togither will shoot the Town Reeve; or dew suthen clever like that!'

"Yeh, I figure I knew exactly what had happened; and I were right. John Bailey were the only one o' those Bertie and me see that night—the only one who know exactly what they are about. The other three that were with him didn't know their ass from their appetite. They were jus' there to do the carrying and the digging, to kinda make the spade handles longer.

When John Bailey went hoom, o' course no one knew. They couldn't find har. Justice, she ha' gone astray."

"So you went over to Fordham and told them where to find her?"

Acky looked at Sarah for a moment or two before replying:

"It weren't as easy as that, gel. We had to hev a confabulation first—a bit o' talk. I knew where she were; and they wanted to find her. So we had to come to an arrangement first."

"What arrangement?"

"Well, there was . . . well, the Town Reeve he call it by some long owd word—suthen. Yeh, I got it: a honorarium! That's it! But I didn't pay regard to what he call it, as long as I got it."

"Honorarium! Acky Flatt, you got the nerve o' the Devil. You mean you asked them for money? How much was it?"

"Never you mind how much! How do you think I bought that rare hog I got from Ipsidge market?"

"Yes, I recall it now," Sarah said grimly. "You went to Fordham and you didn't come home that night!"

Acky grinned: "That were the night I laid on owd Mother Greenfield's pillow, under the hedge about half-way to Fenhall. We were bound to have a celebration after I showed 'em where she were. But when they dug her up, I were whoolly stammed to see how John Bailey had put her away. He done the job parfect: wrappings and tilts and tarpaulins, she were done up better than an Egyptian mummy. She'd been a-lying by that spinney for close on five year; and she took no harm at all. And in less than a week after they'd got her above ground again, there she was a-queening it over the Butter Cross—as spruce and as pure as a maid."

Sarah was silent for some minutes after Acky had finished his story; and he spent them looking idly at the blue, cloud-scudding sky pretending that he wasn't really interested on any comments she would like to make. But at last she asked him:

"You weren't the only one who knew where Justice was to be found. How about Bertie Russett; did he get anything?"

It was now Acky's turn to rake his own thoughts:

"Oh, Bertie knew," he said after a long pause, "he knew right well. But Bertie got nawthen. Bertie never come back! You didn't know that, gel? Fred Partridge, he once told me how it happen. He were out there at the time. It were some big battle out in Africa—El Alamein, I reckon. The tanks were a-moving forard, and Bertie and some others were a-following one of 'em right close. Then the tank got a direct hit. Well, they couldn't find a hair o' Bertie's head. Nawthen, of him or the others."

They were both silent for a while as the bus travelled through suburban streets. Then Acky chuckled again.

"What's it this time?" asked Sarah. "What's funny about that?"

"That Bertie was a rare bo'; and I allus laugh when I think o' that last night's poaching we had togither. A rare bo' was Bertie. But here we are at Ipsidge, gel. I reckon you should ha' paid ma' fare for giving you all thet entertainment."

12

The Rogue Shepherd

"Them bees," Acky said suddenly, "they're never done: they pay no regard to knocking-off time!"

He and Sarah were sitting on a bench outside the back of their cottage enjoying the last rays of a quickly falling sun. Sarah was reading the *Mercury*, the local weekly newspaper, an occupation which filled in the last hour or so of most days in her week. Acky was sitting, forearms on knees, idly watching a late bee, busily working a patch of bergamot and lavender. Sarah went on reading: she had probably not heard Acky's remark; and after a minute or two he spoke again:

"I've been a-thinking about ma young days; they keep a-coming back clearer than yesterday."

"You're getting old, Acky." Sarah folded her newspaper and placed it neatly across her lap. "And I been a-thinking, too, as I read in this *Marcury*—there's a lot about Fordham this week—and I was thinking what you told me about the Justice statue. Don't you ever get pricks o' conscience when you look back to your young days? You got a rare lot o' villainy, one way and another, to answer for. That you have, Acky."

Acky looked at her and grinned, and his grin soon developed into loud laughing. "Ma heart alive!" he said when he'd recovered. "No, no, no! You got it all wrong, gel. My conscience is as healthy as that bee's there. I ha'n't really harmed nobody. I just help property to kind of circulate. Don't you worry! I started as a schemer and I reckon I'll finish up as a schemer. Yeh, never you mind, gel; do we git weaker we git wiser. But I weren't thinking about that Justice: no, about my young times."

"The time you and Lartman cooked that auction sale?"

"Now look here, gel," Acky began as though irritated. But he paused and went on reasonably. "No, ma real young times. We were married at the time of the Lartman business, as you may well recollect; and I were half-way to being an owd man already! No, the time when I were a ragged-trousered lil' owd boy: that's the time I mean, when I just left school. That's the time I were a-thinking on. I niver got round to telling you about that, did I?"

"No, you didn't, Acky," Sarah said kindly, knowing that Acky was far from being cosseted when he was a youngster.

"But this talk about being a willain; I pay no regard to that —to poachin' and a-schemin' wheniver you git a chance. But I tell you this, gel, there was one big cause of it, as you may well know—bad wages. But I made up ma mind I wouldn't starve and I reckon I knew which way the cat were a-going to jump. Instinct, most likely, and a fair bit o' hoss-sense along with it."

He watched the bee closely until it soared away in a loud arc towards the setting sun.

"Yeh, ma real young times when I were a page to a shepherd. And maybe, when I come to think on it, that were one of the reasons I'm the willain you say I am: it was through being 'prentice to such a fine maaster."

"You with the sheep! I always pictured you with the horses. How long were you a page?"

"Yeh, it was only for a short time. I left school at twelve and I went to the horses at fourteen, and I were a-ploughing at fifteen. For two year—from twelve to fourteen—I were page to

Jabez Kennick. I doubt you'd know him. He come from over Barnfield way; and it was at a farm called Doggett's that I went with him. If they put me 'prentice to the Owd Man himself he couldn't ha' taught me more tricks. And I reckon you're lucky, gel"—he turned to Sarah with a sly grin—"that I'm not a wuss willain than you make me out to be. Owd Kennick, he knew every lesson in the Black Book!"

"Tell me about him," said Sarah, sitting back in her chair and placing the newspaper on the floor. She folded her hands on her lap and seemed eager for once to listen to his story.

"Well," said Acky, immediately warming to the rare situation when he had Sarah's full attention, not having to share it with her needlework or the knitting of a pair of pants for one of their many grandchildren, "he were about sixty when I first came to him. He were a tall chap, but a bit bent. He wore a long jacket and cord trousers and allus an old billycock hat, and allus a canvas bag slung over his right shoulder and hanging to his lift side. He went along bent slightly forward; and though he were looking at the ground he'd miss nawthen—when you come to it—in the trees, in the sky, wherever you like. He'd kinda stroll along as if every day had forty-eight hour. But, you wait, jus' you try to keep up when you were a-walking alongside him! When I fust come to him as page I had to trot to keep up with him. He had a dawg—an owd cross-bred—and he knew the lift of Kennick's eyebrow. He'd say nawthen, hardly make a sign, and the dawg would be away like a bullet, allus in the right direction.

"Owd Kennick, he move about the land like a ghost, and his dog were allus at his heel; and nawthen was safe where they passed, anything loose would go into the bag. He wouldn't pass a thing that some day might come in useful. I reckon he *couldn't* pass it! Even an owd bit of iron, a wore-up ploughshare or anything like that, would go into his bag. It were all done so smooth: I reckon he could take the milk out your tea while you were a-setting there a-talking to him. But eggs were the main things that filled his poke. He'd walk through a farmyard, or through a close near by, and he'd come out of it with his poke half full o' eggs. He knew the likely places and he hardly stop in his walk. He'd kinda lope along, bend over, and the eggs were in the bag, all in one movement afore you know what is happening. I reckon many a farmer's wife suffered some bit through having owd Kennick a-loping around their farm.

"The fust lambing season I had with him he had his hut wheeled up to the field where a copse gave good shelter from the north and the east. He'd have everything he wanted up there; but the first night we spend there he say to me, 'Bring a packet o' salt, boy, when you come back from the village.' Salt! Salt! I say. But I soon know next day what it is for: the first chance we have of a break we go to the hut, and he say: 'Got the salt?'; and I took it out o' ma' pocket. He then take a couple o' eggs from his bag, knocked off the top o' one and sprinkled it with the salt; and then he drink it down. 'Here,' he say, handing me the other egg. 'Git that down yew. That'll keep the cowd out.'

"He'd have eggs o' any kind: fowls, bantams, pheasants, partridges; if there'd been ostriches a-setting on that farm, their eggs would have gone into Kennick's poke. Now I'll tell you suthen, gel: some rare birds whose eggs he go arter were nearly his downfall. But that were well after I left him. The farm was a-set on a platform surrounded by a moat—a wery old place I doubt—and the farmer had a notion it were a pity to let all that water goo waste; so as well as ducks and geese he had a lot o' foreign water-birds a-swanning it about that moat; pretty some on 'em were, too. Owd Kennick spent a long time a-watching 'em; then he begin to wonder what their eggs taste like. A couple o' weeks later the farmer, he latch on to what was happening and he set a trap for Kennick. He put some goose's eggs on the side o' the road leading up to the farm—jus' about mid-day when Kennick allus come into the yard to git suthen or other; but allus with his eye to the stray eggs. Now the farmer he get the policeman to come up and wait with him in the stables, looking out through a window where they could see the road and the place where he put the eggs. Along came Owd Jabez; and he see those eggs, and his hand goo out and he were a-stooping down a'most afore he knew it himself, like a dog's tail do shake before he see his dinner. But as he towd me, some bit later: as soon as he really see the eggs close, he know they'd been planted: no bud would ha' laid them there. And he straightened up and placed his hand back in his pocket.

"When he come to the yard, out step the policeman and the farmer ahind him:

" 'Hand me those eggs!' say the policeman.

" 'What eggs?' Kennick say.

"O' course, they sarched him and there were no eggs to be found. They were whoolly stammed. Then after they'd let Kennick goo about his business, they went back down the road and found all the eggs exactly where they planted them. He were too sharp to be pulled as easily as that.

"Like one day I were out with him on this farm, Doggett's, over to Barnfield—a big farm, it were, with a house just like the Veseys', like a mansion. And one morning we were a-seeing to the sheep. We'd got 'em down to a big meadow right a-front of the house. I was walking along (and do you know, gel, I'd began to take after owd Kennick's lope: it take me years to git myself out o' it), I were walking along, and I see suthen in the grass.

" 'There's a pheasant's nest there, Jabez,' I say.

" 'Leave it! Leave it!' he say sharp. 'Don't touch it. Git three hardles and stick 'em up round it!'

"After I'd got the hardles and we were away back in the hut, I ask him why he want the hardles round the pheasant's nest. 'You'll larn, lad,' he say; 'if you picked those eggs up, most likely they'd see you from the house. Instead, I reckon they'll see the hardles!'

" 'Course they did! and the farmer ask him, he say: 'Why have you got those hurdles there, Shepherd?' and Kennick as smooth as butter, he say: to protect the pheasant's nest. And the farmer were some pleased, and he put Kennick up a couple o' notches, and he say: 'Well done! You are the sort of shepherd I like to have about my farm. Just the man!'

"But it weren't only eggs and the odd bagful o' corn when he could get hold of it, but fowls as well. He allus had a dog, o' course, sometimes he had a couple. But this particular dog he'd trained him to pick up a fowl as fast as his master could gather a couple o' eggs. Kennick would be a-going along near a farm where the fowls were a-pecking about: he'd fust look about to see if it were all clear, then he'd jus' say, 'Ssst! Ssst!' between his teeth, and the dog had grabbed a fowl and it were there in the bag in less than a shake o' a lamb's tail.

"I tried this maself once; and it sure gave me a fright. I had this dog with me 'arly one morning, about six o'clock; and we were out away a'most to the next farm (I believe we'd a ewe go astray or suthen line that) and I see a fine cockerel a-working over the field o' stubble not far from the road; and it come to me, 'Shall I try it!' So I say, 'Ssst! Ssst!' like Kennick. And the dog was away and the cock were at ma' feet in no time. Weren't I sceered! I were thirteen and I were in a panic in case we'd been seen. So I stuffed the cock into the bag out o' sight and I take it down to the bottom o' the lane and I hid it in a hole in the hedge. When I go back to the sheep I tell Kennick, and he say, 'Leave it to me: I'll get it,' and he did. He often used to say to me: 'Come up to dinner at mine on Sunday. We got a couple o' hins we're going to see off.'

"But you could say what you like about him, he were the finest shepherd in these parts. None of Kennick's sheep ever had the rot; and if one of 'em got lame, you ma' depend it were a thorn in its foot or suthen like that. He were a right marvel with sheep. He'd be passing a field where there was a part o' the flock, most on 'em maybe a hundred yard away. He'd jus' peek over as he were a-sailing along and then maybe he'd stop: 'There's an owd ewe. Ah! I don't like the look on har. I better goo over. Come with me, boy, I may want you.' He knew. He knew just by the look on her, just the way she were standing or walking or holding har hid, that suthen weren't right!

"Towards the end o' time I were with him, he had a second dog, an old English sheepdawg. And during lambing time Kennick had trained this dawg that he wouldn't let anyone, bar him and me, goo near the sheep. One day the farmer, the farmer himself you see, went up there to have a look at the sheep when Kennick and me were away; and the dogs wouldn't let him goo near. And when he see Kennick later in the day he say: 'It's a fine thing I can't go and have a look at my own sheep!' But the shepherd tell him:

" 'Look, that's how I mean it to be. If anyone want to see the sheep, let 'em come to me fust. I don't want anyone a-poking around and distarbing the sheep when I'm not thar!'

"I recollect one morning with these two dogs, Kennick and me were down in the low on a field called Fen Meadow, and the sheep were a-feedin' quiet. Then Kennick he say to me: 'They been down here long enough: we'll now take 'em up to Dry Field.' He jus' whistle and the two dogs are thar, come from nowhere it seem. One of 'em had been laying up against a stack. And they rounded up those sheep in a jiffy. And once they got 'em moving, this English sheepdawg run back along the gull—the ditch where the stream is—that run through the centre o' the meadow. And I axed Kennick: 'What's he gone back there for?' He say:

" 'To see if an owd sheep ha' got into the gull and can't git out!'

"But he didn't even whistle or say anything to the dawg. He'd just trained him and he went on his own to do the job. Owd Kennick, he take no nonsense, like I tell you with the farmer. I recollect he take me to the first pub I ever been to. It were at this village o' Barnfield. It were one o' the toughest villages along the coast at that time o' day; and there were one pub there, called the *Shepherd and His Dawg*, strange enough. It were the roughest place I ever was in. You'd go in there and they'd drink your beer! And just pick on one of 'em, and it were like a-tarning over a hive o' bees. It were a regular thing if there was a row there at that time o' day, some'un would tarn his mug upside down. That meant: 'Who's for it? I'm ready for anybody.' Another sign were to go outside and shout to whoever you had words with, and then throw your hat into the air. Kennick used to take me in there; but no one turned his mug up to Kennick or throw their hat into the air. They tell me he could use his hands right well when he were younger.

"He went to a good few places round here besides this Doggett's place at Barnfield. He didn't stay many year in one place: he like to be on the move. And most of the farmers knew he were taking stuff off their farms, but either they couldn't catch him—like the man with the rare birds—or they didn't want to, like one particular farmer. He was such a good shepherd that many farmers must ha' thought it would be a-cutting their own nose to spite their face just to sack Kennick. One of 'em knew what was going on; he were called Hubbard. He knew right well he couldn't sack Kennick; but he had to do suthen because he was a-lifting so much stuff. So one day this Hubbard say to Kennick:

" 'I'm selling my flock, Shepherd. You'd better take a month's notice.'

"So he sold his sheep; paid Kennick off, and got rid of him that way. Now this Kennick, when he left Hubbard, went down to a place in Essex. One day, some bit later, Hubbard's son go down to Essex to a sale; and he see Kennick at the sale and he go up to him and say:

" 'How are you getting on with your sheep: have you got a good place, Shepherd?'

"And o' course the lad were older than he was the time Kennick work for his father, and the shepherd didn't recognize him, and he say: 'Yeh,' he say, 'middling. But I niver have such a good place as I have up thar in Suffolk with a farmer by the name o' Hubbard.'

"The lad told his father when he got hoom; and the old man laughed: 'He was right. He had a good place with me! I just like him to carry on his back all the stuff he took off this farm. That would make him bend over a good deal more than he's bending now!'

" 'But he was a good shepherd, Dad.'

" 'Yes, he was, Son. But when you've said that you've said all!' "

Acky paused and stretched his arms above his head: "It take you back, gel. It take you back. And you can't rightly add it all up, 'cos it's nigh on sixty year agoo; and yet it's as clear as that sun a-going down over thar, a-hind Mrs. Vesey's elms."

"But what happened to the shepherd? Did you ever hear tell of him after that?"

"Yeh, I hear he die some years back and he were buried down

there in Essex. But I didn't tell you, gel: after he give up the sheep he live in a village atween Colchester and Chelmsford. He used to spend a rare lot of his time down there a-leaning over his gate, watching the world goo by. He let his beard grow, and he blend right well into the landscape, you could say"; Acky chuckled to himself, "like he allus did when he were in Suffolk! Then, one day, an artist fellow come along and he see Kennick and he want to paint his picture. He come back a few times; and the next thing they hear this picture is in an exhibition. And who do you think owd Kennick were supposed to be? I wouldn't believe it but it's as true as I'm talking to you right now."

"I don't know," Sarah said testily. "You're the one who's telling the story. You tell me!"

"No story, gel. This is the truth, as true as Kennick were a right schemer. They painted him as God the Father."

"Acky!" Sarah said, deeply shocked.

"No, gel; there's no disrespect. I'm just telling you what happen. And in a way it were right just, like I tell you: Kennick was a right good shepherd—right to the end of his day; and he allus give a fair deal to his sheep."

Glossary

ahind: Behind

allus: Always

a-physicing: Taking physic or medicine; cf. "physical gentlemen" for doctors

ax: Ask, as in Chaucer's *Canterbury Tales*

bait: Horse-fodder

billy-cock: A hard felt hat with a high crown

binder-cord: Cord used to tie up sheaves of corn when cut by modern reaping-machines

boons: Bones

bor: Mate or friend (pronounced *boo*)

bud: A bird

chance-times: Now and then, occasionally

chaw-porks: Country-dwellers (chew-porks); a reference to the amount of pig's meat in the countryman's diet

comb: A corn measure (four bushels)

cowd: Cold

do: Often used conditionally, giving the sense of *if you do*

draught: A drawing, or plan; cf. draughtsman

fare: To feel, seem, appear; a difficult word to define as it is used idiomatically, with fine gradations of meaning, in many different contexts

fold-pritch: Heavy steel bar once used by shepherds to make holes in the ground to take their sheep-hurdles

fravelings or *frazlings:* Threads or "ends" left dangling from a skirt-hem or frayed trouser-bottom

fule: Fool

fust: First

going-ahid (ahead): Giving way to angry talk, "creating" or "going on"; getting *het up* (*q.v.*)

Glossary

gull: A deep ditch made by a stream
har: Her
hardles: Hurdles
haysel: The hay-harvest; *lit.* hay-time (*hay-sele*)
het: Heated
hid: Head
hin: Hen
hodmedod: Snail
hoom: Home
knoll: Small green at centre of a village; often triangular in shape
know: Knowledge
mawkin or *malkin:* A scarecrow
mort: a great number
mun: Must, as in "I mun goo"; cf. Scottish *maun*
nawthen: Nothing
net'us: Neat-house; neat is O.E. for cattle; the byre or shippon
nobble: Tamper with, get hold of dishonestly
owd: Old
page: A shepherd's boy or apprentice
passon: Parson
peek: A look (pronounced *paak*)
poke: A bag
pong: Smell
pull: To summon to court, to fine
putter: To nag
right: Often has the force of *very*; cf. Biblical "and that right early"
rile: Annoy, irritate
rum: Odd, strange
scrabble: Scratch or erase
sele: Time; "to give the s. of the day" to greet someone in passing
set: Sit
shod: Shed
singling: To single a crop is to thin it out so that individual plants have room to mature
snaffle: Purloin, pinch, steal
squit: Rubbish, worthless material, nonsense
stammed: Amazed, astounded
stetch: Portion of a ploughed field in between two water-furrows; a land or rig

Glossary

suthen: Something

tiddy: Small

tidily (*good-tidily* or *half-tidy*)*:* Smoothly: "It's going g.t." means "It's doing very well"

tilt: Waterproof covering for stacks, etc.

together: See *you together*

trapsing or *traipsing:* To walk or go about apparently without much aim

travelling-woman: A *traveller* is a gipsy

tumbril: A two-wheeled farm-cart

water-boots: Rubber boots or Wellingtons

will-jill: A masculine woman

whoolly (wholly)*:* Altogether, as in *w. stammed*, completely astounded

windy: Angry

wort: Malt liquid before it has fermented into beer

yard: Garden or enclosure; Chaucer's *yerd* (*The Nun's Priest's Tale*)

you together: You (plural); to distinguish it from you (singular); *You all* is used for the plural in some other dialects